# Wilderness Survival

## ~ Volume 1 ~

## Daniel Ploof

# Trail Route ~ Volume 1

# Trials & Temptations

I love that quote because it affirms my imperfections and testifies even a "C" is a passing grade! However, am I just trying to get by with a passing grade, or am I committed to investing the blood, sweat and tears required to be the man God calls me to be? Could it be I am lukewarm, chickening out when the heat gets turned up in the kitchen? Honestly, I'm just a chicken afraid of falling head-first into the deep fryer of God's Word! More often than I care to admit, I'm afraid of change and would rather maintain status quo because it is familiar. I can easily settle there and I believe men as a whole in the Christian church suffer the same poor attitude because they're tired, worn out, or too lazy to put in the hard work necessary to change for the better.

There is a saying many who walk the path of addiction recovery identify with: "Sick and tired of being sick and tired." What it communicates is that the pleasures of this world are meaningless if we're trying to fill the empty void in our heart and soul with anything except God. Do you know that feeling? Do you know it personally, or is it a vague mirage on the horizon you're bent on walking toward until you find out? I've been there. I've tasted the filth of my sin and the consequences which inevitably come with it. I've tested the "grass is greener on the other side" theory and found myself lost and alone in a desert. I've played with my "desires of the flesh" fire and gotten burnt. Bottom-line, I've learned first-hand that change only comes when you make the conscious decision that you're sick and tired of being sick and tired of the same 'ol, same 'ol, mundane status quo for your life, marriage and family. Thankfully, though, God does His most powerful, transforming work in the valley!

This curriculum is a buffet line of conviction and surrender as we begin to recognize the depravity of our hearts and minds through the exercise of physically writing down our answers and discussing them with our wives. It will reveal a man's true thoughts, feelings, perceptions and actions, and then compare them to the absolute truth of Scripture which illuminates truth and exposes lies. Satan will do everything in his power to disrupt and divert a man's attention from completing this study. Therefore, we must be prayerfully guarded and consciously aware of our surroundings, both physically and spiritually, at all times.

I pray our hearts are challenged as we commit to finish **Volume-1** and **Volume-2** of this study no matter the cost. There will always be reasons why we should not start or finish it. Therefore, we must lean on the body of Christ because we'll need support and recognition that we're not alone, and others will need to be reminded as well. Therefore, let us not fear the marriage grenade but rather protect our wives and children by sacrificing our pride for them. And may we aim higher, allowing the refiner's fire to burn away all our impurities as we embark on a journey of **WILDERNESS SURVIVAL** together. The time for change is now if indeed you're truly sick and tired of being sick and tired.

# Survival Essentials

## SPIRITUAL LEADERSHIP

This study is specifically designed for men, currently married, engaged, or in preparatory courtship for marriage, who are eager to accept their God-given role as head of the household. As spiritual leaders, we're called to lead our families by living a God-honoring life which requires courage, humility and a willingness to take initiative. As men, we should be willing to lay down our pride for our families, by investing our time and doing the work by sacrificing our insecurities, thoughts, emotions, perspectives and experiences on topics related to life and marriage. This is an opportunity for us to be challenged and transformed through God's Word by discussing our answers with our wives during the week, and coming together in a small discipleship group of men ready to discuss and share what we've learned by sharpening one another's character and countenance.

## PATIENCE & FORTITUDE

This study will try and test the patience and fortitude of every man who applies himself. Temptations to give up will be intense but we cannot yield to our flesh. Keep in mind, success is not about right and wrong answers but wrestling with the application of God's Word so that unresolved issues do not become wedges of dissention in the home. A man who embraces this study will be pushed to the brink spiritually, but his family and marriage will be transformed because of it. The key is being on guard against the enemy because Satan thrives in secrecy and isolation. Therefore, casting fear and doubt aside is the defining mark of a man bent on creating a healthier home and marriage regardless of how long the process takes and how difficult it is.

## ACCOUNTABILITY

Wives play a crucial role in this study—not as bystanders, but helpers. No one should know a man better than his wife, therefore her input, honesty and understanding are critical to success. CAUTION: Some women have never been given the opportunity to offer accountability or share their honest perspective with their husbands, so they may be timid or fearful at first. Conversely, other wives may respond completely opposite. Remember, it is sanctification we're after, directly through the husband and indirectly through the wife by her loving example of God's absolute truth lived out by her support, understanding and forgiveness. Therefore, give her free reign to offer perspective and value her honest input unconditionally with humility and respect. It is also imperative we embark on this journey with a small group of men to avoid pitfalls of isolation. The enemy aims to isolate us and this study will thrust us into a wilderness environment quickly, but fellowship with trusted men diffuses Satan's tactics and provides a hedge of protection critical to survival.

## DISCRETION

Know that we must always speak truth in love and not crush our wives with raw honesty. Often times, the freedom of releasing hidden thoughts, sins and struggles is a transfer of weight from our shoulders to theirs. Therefore, we must be gentle and love them in an understanding way, acknowledging they are demonstrating incredible humility, trust and restraint watching us fight spiritual battles in order to be conformed to the image of Jesus Christ. Make no mistake, these precious women are sacrificing their sanity by shouldering the weight of spiritual warfare while God refines our character—an incredible gift for which must be eternally thankful.

# Survival Essentials

## VULNERABILITY

A common misconception is men need to be more transparent when men actually need to be more vulnerable. Transparency conveys, "I'll share with you who I am to the extent I feel comfortable." Vulnerability takes it a step further and thrusts a man into discomfort because he doesn't know how his thoughts, feelings and actions will be received beforehand. When we're vulnerable true humility is present and God performs transformational miracles through our complete surrender. Again, we need to be very sensitive and careful not to blindside our wives without proper support. Seek Biblical counseling immediately if the information you are sharing is severe (ex: adultery, substance abuse, financial downfalls, etc.) A wise man will always seek the wisdom and discernment of many Biblical counselors. Utilize the body of Christ and local church without hesitation in this area.

## FORGIVENESS

Forgiveness cannot be understated. As we struggle through each topic, we'll face the realization we've blown it more often than not, and that in our own strength we do not measure up. Therefore, we can't complete this journey alone. Only by the indwelling power of the Holy Spirit will a saved-by-grace, not-by-works, born-again, man of God be able to survive the wilderness and bind the schemes of the enemy who seeks to destroy us and our marriages. Our wives will also find themselves challenged to forgive our mistakes and failures with each passing trail marker. Keep in mind, the transferred weight of sin is real and can destroy a woman's psyche. Therefore, we must build a solid support network of men as we engage this study because we all need one another's support and encouragement to survive.

## COURAGE

Be courageous, not fearful! God's constant encouragement to Joshua as he led Israel into the promised land was courage (Deuteronomy 31:23). We should adhere to that same message when exposing our honest thoughts. Choosing to write a vague answer instead of an honest one only wastes time. Change occurs when we decide to own our failures and shortcomings. If we offer broken hearts to God, He will honor our sacrifice. However, if we hold back our first fruits, He will withhold His blessing from us. We must tithe our best and allow God to transform us from the inside-out by giving Him free reign to extract the cancer of sin within our hearts. "Be strong and courageous. Do not fear or be in dread of them, for it is the Lord your God who goes with you. He will not leave you or forsake you" (Deuteronomy 31:6).

## RESTRAINT

The urge to get defensive on this journey will be intense, especially when we're instructed to discuss our answers with our wives and discipleship group. Remember, vulnerability is not a sign of weakness. Quite the opposite! Vulnerability requires meekness which takes quiet strength to open our hearts and minds for all to see. Moses is a tremendous example of restraint because he displayed meekness when leading the Israelites through the wilderness. He trusted and obeyed God even when his own people were not cooperating, but also suffered an incredible consequence for not restraining his anger as well.

# Survival Essentials

## CHANGE

God is the author of change, but by the power of the Spirit dwelling in us, as born-again Christians, we have the power to accept or reject change. What an amazing truth! However, when we believe Satan's lie which assumes lasting change can survive apart from God, we undermine God's sovereignty that He is in control, not us. It is difficult to relinquish control of our lives when things are falling apart because we tend to hold onto what is familiar, even if it destroys us. Yet Scripture declares that with God all things are possible (Mark 10:27), because He loves us far more than we could ever imagine with an everlasting love which endures our greatest failures. Change is definitely attainable for the man who trusts God and submits to His authority in complete surrender and obedience to His Word.

## ABSOLUTE TRUTH

We must hold firm to God's absolute truth because the wilderness is meant to isolate us, even within a small group of men. We cannot come to grips with our sin, temptations, insecurities, biases, desires, etc., without spending 1-on-1 time in relationship with God the Father. In the context of the wilderness, though, Satan enters the picture and seeks to whisper lies into our minds to break our fellowship with God. We would be wise to remember Jesus' conversation with Satan in the wilderness, for He overcame temptation by quoting Scripture. Therefore, by the power of the Holy Spirit living within us, we can too! We are guaranteed Satan does not want us to become more like Christ, so he will fiercely tempt us because he knows our weaknesses better than we do. Our only hope of survival is found in God's Holy Word, which illuminates our path and extinguishes the fiery arrows aimed to wound and destroy us.

## INTENTIONALITY

As we journey through the wilderness, let us be intentionally focused on what we feed our minds. Culture seeks to bombard us with lies which undermine the work God desires for us to accomplish. Therefore, we must be on guard and proactively filter out worldly lies and philosophies. Turn the TV off, screen movies, ignore provocative billboards or advertising, limit internet browsing, turn off social media, filter news information, guard against potentially compromising, interpersonal communications (1-on-1 chat, text, email, social media, etc.) with other women especially, and wisely consider everything we allow our minds to feed upon daily.

## PRAYER

Prayer was the single most important aspect of Jesus' devotional life. His fellowship with God was critical and should be a convicting reminder to us as well. Therefore, we must position ourselves under God's authority and lean not on our own understanding but acknowledge Him in all our ways so He would make our paths straight. Only then will we be able to pray: 1. That our hearts would be strong and courageous; 2. That our wives would help and support us while they wrestle with spiritual warfare each day on our behalf; 3. That our children would recognize a Godly, fatherly example in our behavior; and 4. That our friends and family would forgive our sins and the consequences of our actions which directly and indirectly impact them.

# Trail Markers

Make no mistake, this battle is only beginning! For we may gain victory in 20-weeks from now by finishing **WILDERNESS SURVIVAL, Volume-1**, but the war rages on as we prepare our hearts and minds to conquer **WILDERNESS SURVIVAL, Volume-2** and reach our summit. Keep in mind, our spiritual enemy is far more sophisticated in his schemes than we can fathom and will exploit our weaknesses at all cost. Therefore, we must be diligent to feast upon the absolute truth of God's Word and the power of prayer to sustain our lives and remain in frequent and consistent fellowship with other brothers in Christ. Satan will mainly focus his immediate attention on targeting what we assume is our greatest strength, because if he can break us there he can essentially have free reign over our entire life. However, if we know this up front, we'll make wiser decisions ahead of time by anticipating his plan of attack and securing our defenses ahead of time.

It is also imperative we maintain teachable spirits, allowing our wives to speak truth into our hearts regarding our character. We all have blind spots, but God in His wisdom equipped us with wives who can hold us accountable if we give them the attention they deserve and value their input. Be forewarned! We cannot assume our wives' accountability is inspired by malicious motives. Therefore, we must sift out any selfish intentions they may have or we assume they have, and seek to apply the truth of their feedback no matter how hard the pill is to swallow. For in the end, our wives are our allies for productive heart change unto Christ, not bottlenecks to our desires.

 **CAMPFIRE SYMBOLS** are intentionally placed throughout this study to help build spiritual intimacy with your wife. Take full advantage of these discussion opportunities as they can also be used as discussion starters for your men's discipleship group.

It is paramount we are intentional to seek forgiveness with great humility and reverence unto God, our wives, and our children. True humility is infectious and can diffuse a tense and volatile situation. Therefore, we cannot allow Satan to drive wedges within our homes by holding firm to pride. We must admit all wrongs, acknowledge our shortcomings, and seek forgiveness. As spiritual leaders, our wives and children need to see humility displayed in us so they have a Biblical example to follow. We will never regret any opportunities God provides to strengthen our families by humbling ourselves and sacrificing our pride for their benefit.

Finally, we must strongly consider the legacy we will leave our families as a result of prioritizing our marriages and children. No man who humbly applies himself to completing this study will regret the investment he is making, because he knows each one of these issues has manifested itself to some degree or another within his lifetime and/or marriage. He knows he needs to address them repeatedly moving forward. Therefore, this study has the potential to radically transform a man from the inside-out if he will allow God free reign over his life. God's intent to sanctify us into the image of Jesus is for our benefit and His glory, for His love far surpasses our feeble attempts to fully understand because it is not of this world. It is unchanging for all eternity and we are the beneficiaries of that eternal promise.

I pray we come to know our Lord and Savior in a new and profound way because God longs for intimate fellowship with His children, and that opportunity is unconditionally available to us in this wilderness study. When we accepted Christ, we were given a new identity as children of God, indwelt by the power of the Holy Spirit. Therefore, we can proclaim in faith that we can do all things through Christ who strengthens us because His Spirit dwells in us and gives us supernatural power to radically transform our lives and homes for His purpose and glory, and ultimately our benefit.

# Survivor Stories

The following "survivor stories" came from the original test groups of this curriculum with one man in particular, Jerry, having a profound impact on my heart. From Day-1, Jerry dove into both volumes and followed the designed format by answering questions on his own, discussing them with his wife, Pat, and meeting with his weekly discipleship group to share what he had learned. What struck me from their feedback was they humbled themselves like newlyweds and embraced this study as an opportunity to strengthen their marriage. There was no "been there, done that" attitude, but rather a willingness to flush out their thoughts and opinions on a myriad of topics while filtering them through each other's perspective and God's Word for wisdom and discernment. They embraced vulnerability and used this study as a catalyst to strengthen their marriage. Roughly 4-years later, this beautiful couple passed away within weeks of one another, over 60+ years of marriage under their belt. Their lives and more importantly, their marriage, stand as a testament to the saving power of Jesus Christ and how they loved one another. Personally-speaking, their input regarding this entire study will forever be treasured confirmation that heart change is possible for any man willing to humble himself, surrender to God's sovereign will and authority, and journey deep into "Wilderness Survival" mode for the sake of his family.

"God used the topics to inspire me to be a better husband, father, and follower of Christ.
I find that I already miss the daily challenge of a new topic to chew on and apply.
This study proved to be a good grindstone to sharpen areas of my life that had become dull."

- Steve -

"I expected to be challenged and grow spiritually, and I have done that.
God has caused me to look at and deal with things in my life that I normally don't do.
What has been good and helpful is my wife and I have been talking and discussing
things in our life/marriage that we've needed to talk about.
My wife has really enjoyed discussing some of the questions each week.
She even said, 'I hate to see the study end!'
The study has caused me to be more committed in my time with the Lord each day.
I've had a more positive attitude during the study, seeing God at work more each day
and how He is continuing to bless our marriage and grow us closer together."

- Jerry -

"I have loved Jerry during this study and I am sorry that it is over. I like him going over the
questions with me. It has given us an opportunity to discuss things we don't usually talk about.
He has been more verbal about his love for me. I know it, but it is very nice to hear it out loud.
I know that our relationship is a work in progress just like our relationship with Jesus.
We've been married 57 years and this study has been good for our marriage!
I am madly in love with my husband, but this study has enhanced this love."

- Jerry's Wife (Pat) -

# Trailhead Perspective

"If a man doubts his manliness, he needs only to believe what is already true.
God created him to be a man and to live as a man by being strong and keeping His Word.

Even a man that the world would consider weak, feeble, and the least "manly"
can be stronger than many in the world if he believes God and keeps His commandments.

He does not need to take a trip to the wilderness
and wait for a voice from heaven to declare to his soul that he is a man.

He does not have to wait for his father or some father figure
to somehow bestow "man-ness" upon him.

He doesn't have to prove to himself or to others that he has what it takes
to do whatever the world or he himself deems is important and manly.

Masculinity is given by God to men, and men must live it out Biblically
rather than perverting it and redefining it in worldly, carnal, and selfish terms."

- Brent Barnett -

"BE MEN!
In courage; not cowards, turning our back on the foe, or giving way in danger, or reproach,
or evil days. In solidity; not shifting or shadowy, but immoveable as the rock. In strength;
as the man is, so is his strength. Be strong! In wisdom. Foolishness is with childhood,
wisdom with manhood. Speak and act with wisdom, as men. In ripeness. The faculties of men
are ripe, both for thinking and working. They speak ripe words, think ripe thoughts,
plan and execute ripe things. In understanding be men! In all things – what you do,
and what you refrain from doing, be men. Act the manly part – let nothing effeminate,
luxurious, sickly, childish, puny, little, narrow be seen about you. Christianity makes men,
not babes. Adorn the doctrine of Christ by your manliness. In the Church, in the world,
in business, in conversation, in prosperity, and adversity, [act] like men!
Let no man despise you; and let no man despise the Gospel because of you."

- Horatius Bonar -

# Theology - Day 1

It is impossible to have any discussion on the application of Scripture without addressing the ultimate question of who God is. A man must know his Creator, what role God plays in his life, and what connection they have to one another. Therefore, a man must know his theology is firm without holes or blemishes which could undermine or discredit his faith. He must be able to articulate what he believes about God, because what he believes shapes who he is as a man. I cannot overstate that loving my wife and children is futile without knowing God personally. For if God is who He says He is throughout the pages of Scripture, I am empowered by the Holy Spirit to love and serve others unconditionally as I willingly obey His Word and completely surrender my life to Him by grace through faith alone in Jesus Christ.

- Who do you believe God is? _____
  _____
  _____

- Read Isaiah 40:9-31. What does this passage of Scripture convey about the greatness of God?

  - _____
  - _____
  - _____
  - _____
  - _____
  - _____

- What attributes of God are found in Psalm 145 (Who is the Lord God)?

  - _____  • _____
  - _____  • _____
  - _____  • _____
  - _____  • _____

- John 3:16-17 says: _____
  _____
  _____

  - Therefore, what is God's desire for your life? _____
    _____

- Read Ephesians 2:1-10 and answer the following questions. What is...

  - My eternal plight (v. 1-3): _____
  _____

  - God's provision (v. 4-7): _____
  _____

  - God's plan of salvation (v. 8-10): _____
  _____

- Have you accepted Jesus Christ as Lord & Savior? _____ Why or why not? _____
  _____
  _____

  - Why is it important to reconcile yourself eternally to God? _____
  _____

> "Theology is not a philosophical pursuit of abstract speculations about God.
> It is in fact the examination of that which God has revealed to us.
> As faithful students of the Word of God, we are, by necessity, students of theology.
> The two are not at odds with each other; rather they serve to complement one another.
> Whereas the Word of God is the foundation of our knowledge, theology is the expression of our
> knowledge. Thus, the study of God cannot be separated from the Word of God."
>
> - Burk Parsons -

- What is your greatest takeaway from today's study? _____
  _____
  _____
  _____

> "I, I am he who blots out your transgressions for my own sake, and I will not remember your sins."
> - Isaiah 43:25 -

- What does this verse mean to you? _____
  _____
  _____
  _____

# Theology - Day 2

- What impact does a saving relationship with Jesus Christ mean to you?

    - As a man: _____

    _____

    - As a husband: _____

    _____

    - As a father: _____

    _____

    - As a son: _____

    _____

    - As a friend: _____

    _____

    - As an employee/employer: _____

    _____

- How does John 15:18 bring comfort as you strive to live out "saving faith" because of Jesus?

    - _____

    - _____

    - _____

    - _____

- Read Psalm 139:1-16. What difference does it make that God knows all there is to know about you? _____

    _____

    _____

- Read Jeremiah 1:5. What does it mean God knew you before He formed you? _____

    _____

    _____

    - How can this verse impact and improve the amount of quality time you spend with God? _____

    _____

    _____

- Read Jeremiah 29:11. How does this verse change your perspective regarding God's sovereign plan and purpose for your life? _____

  _____

  _____

- From your perspective, what character qualities best describe what it means to be a Christian?

  - _____       - _____       - _____

  - _____       - _____       - _____

    - Do these qualities describe yourself? _____ Why or why not? _____

      _____

      _____

---

"A true and faithful Christian does not make holy living an accidental thing. It is his great concern. As the business of the soldier is to fight, so the business of the Christian is to be like Christ."

- Jonathan Edwards -

"If you do not listen to Theology, that will not mean that you have no ideas about God. It will mean that you have a lot of wrong ones – bad, muddled, out-of-date ideas. For a great many of the ideas about God which are trotted out as novelties today are simply the ones which real Theologians tried centuries ago and rejected."

- C.S. Lewis -

---

- What is your greatest takeaway from today's study? _____

  _____

  _____

  _____

---

"I call heaven and earth to witness against you today, that I have set before you life and death, blessing and curse. Therefore choose life, that you and your offspring may live, loving the LORD your God, obeying his voice and holding fast to him, for he is your life and length of days."

- Deuteronomy 30:19-20 -

---

- What does this verse mean to you? _____

  _____

  _____

  _____

# Absolute Truth - Day 1

When the Bible is substituted for books written or inspired by a theme or issue spoken of in the Bible, Scripture shifts from a position of centrality in a believer's life to secondary by the sheer amount of time spent in each. Secondary resources may be extremely profound and full of insight, but they can never replace the absolute truth of Holy Scripture. The Bible is more than just a book. It is a living and breathing entity, inspired by God's Spirit and manifested through Christ. The day I realized Jesus and the Bible are inter-connected is the day I stopped viewing the Bible as a man-made set of rules and began finding freedom in the truth of Christ. In other words, religion transformed into relational faith. Truly, life is made new through the pages of Scripture to the man who realizes this profound truth.

- Do you believe the Bible is absolute truth? _____ Why or why not? _____
  _____
  _____

- Are there any verses in Scripture you either completely disagree with, somewhat disagree with, or do not fully understand which directly impact your faith walk? Which verses or topics?

  - _____          - _____

  - _____          - _____

  - _____          - _____

  - How do they affect the validity of Scripture in your mind? _____
    _____
    _____

  - What impact do they have (positive or negative) on your relationship with God? _____
    _____
    _____

- What is your first reaction when you read Hebrews 4:12? _____
  _____

  - How would you paraphrase this verse in your own words? _____
    _____

- Why is John 8:31-32 so hard to live out? _____
  _____
  _____

- Read John 1:14. Why is Jesus referred to as the "Word?" _____
  _____
  _____

  - What is the glory of Jesus? _____
    _____

  - How is John 1:1 related to John 1:14? _____
    _____
    _____

- What role do grace and truth (John 1:14) play in the Gospel message of salvation?

  - Grace: _____
    _____

  - Truth: _____
    _____

> "The one most valuable lesson humanity ought to have learned from philosophy is that it is impossible to make sense of truth without acknowledging God as the necessary starting point."
>
> - John MacArthur -
>
> "Truth is so obscure in these times, and falsehood so established, that, unless we love the truth, we cannot know it."
>
> - Blaise Pascal -

- What is your greatest takeaway from today's study? _____
  _____
  _____
  _____

> "In the beginning was the Word, and the Word was with God, and the Word was God."
> - John 1:1 -

- What does this verse mean to you? _____
  _____
  _____
  _____

# Absolute Truth - Day 2

- Read Psalm 19:7-11. What words does the Psalmist use to describe God and His Word?

    - _____
    - _____
    - _____

    - _____
    - _____
    - _____

    - Which quality do you struggle relating to most? _____ Why? _____

      _____

      _____

- What fears/insecurities/excuses hinder you from reading the Bible on a daily basis?

    - _____

    - _____

- How can Ephesians 5:25-27 change your approach to Scripture as a husband sanctifying your wife? _____

  _____

  _____

  _____

- When you speak truth in love to your wife, what character qualities in you must be displayed?

    - ( _____ ) Why? _____

      _____

    - ( _____ ) Why? _____

      _____

    - ( _____ ) Why? _____

      _____

- When your wife speaks truth in love to you, what qualities about her distract you from listening?

    - ( _____ ) Why? _____

      _____

    - ( _____ ) Why? _____

      _____

    - ( _____ ) Why? _____

      _____

- Create a list of individuals whose input and opinions influence your decision-making the most.

  - _____  • _____  • _____  • _____

    - Whose opinion is the strongest? _____ Most agreeable? _____

    - Whose opinion carries the most weight spiritually? _____ Why? _____

    _____

    _____

    - Whose input is the hardest to receive? _____ Why? _____

    _____

    _____

    - Do you seek wisdom from God's Word BEFORE or AFTER you ask others? _____

    - Why is it important to seek discernment from Scripture first before asking others? _____

    _____

    _____

> "Jesus did not accept religious people. In fact, He kept His fiercest threats for them.
> You see, Jesus was not about sentimentality; He was about truth.
> Jesus is truth personified. He is the living manifestation of the holy law of God, and as such,
> He perfectly understood that religion, spiritual teaching, contrary to the truth comes from
> hell and sends people there. Anything but the truth is a damning deception that has the
> greatest power to destroy souls forever because it gives the illusion that all is well."
>
> - John MacArthur -

- What is your greatest takeaway from today's study? _____

_____

_____

_____

> "Every word of God proves true; he is a shield to those who take refuge in him."
> - Proverbs 30:5 -

- What does this verse mean to you? _____

_____

_____

_____

# Faith ~ Day 1

Faith is the only foundation a marriage should be built upon to ensure our marital covenants have the best opportunity to succeed. For God is the author of faith and we must understand, comprehend and ultimately accept Christ's atoning sacrifice if we're to know what it truly means to love our wives as Christ loved the church. It is impossible to underestimate the importance of genuine, humble faith and how twisted a man can become without it. I personally lived a life full of hypocrisy long enough to know faith is hollow without humility. Fortunately, I married a woman who passionately loves God because her Christ-like example is God's daily provision, showing me how I must love Him first and foremost if I'm to be the selfless man, husband and father He calls me to be. Faith is the doorway to freedom.

- In your own words, define faith. _____
  _____
  _____

- Do you consider yourself a man of faith? _____ Why or why not? _____
  _____
  _____

- Read Hebrews 11:1-3 and 1 Corinthians 13:13. Define the relationship between faith, hope and love.

  - Faith and Hope: _____
    _____

  - Faith and Love: _____
    _____

- Read Romans 8:1-11. Where/How is the Holy Spirit actively working in your marriage and family?

  - Where: _____ How: _____
    _____
    _____

  - Where: _____ How: _____
    _____
    _____

  - Where: _____ How: _____
    _____
    _____

- Read Romans 6:15-23. What doubts do you wrestle with regarding God's forgiveness of your sins?

  - _____     - _____

  - _____     - _____

  - Has doubt ever tempted you to lose faith altogether? _____ How so? _____
    _____
    _____

- How do you forgive yourself knowing you continue to sin each day? _____
  _____
  _____

  - How can your wife pray for you in this area? _____
    _____

> "The man who puts his trust in the Lord sees the pleasures of sin in a new light. For he sees the evil which follows them by noting the agonies which they brought upon our Lord when He bore our sins in His own body on the tree. Without faith a man says to himself, "This sin is a very pleasant thing, why should I not enjoy it? Surely I may eat this fruit, which looks so charming and is so much to be desired." The flesh sees honey in the drink, but faith at once perceives that there is poison in the cup. Faith spies the snake in the grass and gives warning of it. Faith remembers death, judgment, the great reward, the just punishment and that dread word, eternity."
>
> - Charles Spurgeon -

- What is your greatest takeaway from today's study? _____
  _____
  _____
  _____

> "I have been crucified with Christ. It is no longer I who live, but Christ who lives in me. And the life I now live in the flesh I live by faith in the Son of God, who loved me and gave himself for me."
>
> - Galatians 2:20 -

- What does this verse mean to you? _____
  _____
  _____
  _____

# Faith - Day 2

- In what ways has your faith in Christ sustained or saved your life/marriage?

  - _____
    _____

  - _____
    _____

- In what ways has your lack of faith in Christ hindered or plagued your life/marriage?

  - _____
    _____

  - _____
    _____

- Read John 20:24-29. What message does Jesus convey to Thomas that you need to hear? _____
  _____
  _____

- Read Hebrews 11. What encouragements can you gain from Holy Scripture by faith?

  - _____
  - _____
  - _____
  - _____
  - _____
  - _____

- Read Matthew 17:14-20. In what areas of your life/marriage are you lacking "mustard seed" faith?

  - ( _____ ) Why? _____
    _____
    _____

  - ( _____ ) Why? _____
    _____
    _____

- Read 1 Kings 19:11-12. How has the Lord revealed His faithfulness toward you?

  - In signs and wonders: _____

    _____

    _____

  - In a still, small voice: _____

    _____

    _____

  - When do you struggle most recognizing God's presence? _____

    _____

- What spiritual disciplines are needed to hear God's voice in your life? Circle your weakest area.

  - _____   • _____   • _____   • _____

> "We do not believe in belief any more than we have faith in faith. We believe the gospel, and we have faith in Christ. Our beliefs have substance and our faith has an object."
>
> - Albert Mohler -
>
> "We took the Prince of glory, we scourged him at the whipping post, we hounded him through the streets, having no compassion on him. We took our sins and drove them like nails through his hands and feet. We lifted him high up on the cross of our transgressions, and then we pierced his heart through with the spear of our unbelief."
>
> -Charles Spurgeon -

- What is your greatest takeaway from today's study? _____

  _____

  _____

  _____

> "Not to us, O LORD, not to us, but to your name give glory, for the sake of your steadfast love and your faithfulness!"
>
> - Psalm 115:1 -

- What does this verse mean to you? _____

  _____

  _____

  _____

# Spiritual Warfare - Day 1

In all our well-intentioned efforts to live for Christ, there remains an equally intentional enemy of God who feeds our flesh with tempestuous thoughts, feelings and emotions to draw us into isolation. Satan is the author of all sin and evil in this world and his primary purpose is to destroy the kingdom of God one soul at a time. It begins with shifting our attention away from God as our ultimate authority to our flesh reigning supreme in our lives, manifested through a melting pot of sins. However, God's love through Christ's death on the cross atones for every sin in this world to the one who humbly repents and turns away from his rebellion. God's Word has taught me that the more I take spiritual warfare lightly, the more susceptible I become to let my guard down, surrender to the enemy, and accept defeat.

- Read Matt. 4:1, 16:23; John 8:39-47; 2 Cor. 11:14; 2 Thess. 2:9; 1 Peter 5:8; 1 John 3:8; Rev. 12:9.

    - Who is Satan? _____
    _____

    - What is his purpose? _____
    _____

    - How does he accomplish his mission? _____
    _____

- Read Genesis 3. What lies does Satan entice you to consider which tempt you to doubt God's Word?

    - _____
    - _____
    - _____

- Genesis 3 magnifies Adam's greatest sin as a husband by how he failed to protect his wife. Where in your marriage do you struggle protecting your wife from spiritual warfare?

    - Where? _____ How? _____
    _____
    _____

    - Where? _____ How? _____
    _____
    _____

    - Why is it harder to protect spiritually vs. physically? _____
    _____

- What is Satan using to drive a wedge between you and your wife?

- Physically: _____
  _____

- Emotionally: _____
  _____

- Spiritually: _____
  _____

- Children: _____
  _____

- Season of Life: _____
  _____

- Outside Influences: _____
  _____

> "Now, beloved, if our Lord and Master selected this true Jerusalem blade of the Word of God, let us not hesitate for a moment but grasp and hold fast this one true weapon of the saints in all times. Cast away the wooden sword of carnal reasoning. Trust not in human eloquence but arm yourselves with the solemn declaration of God, who cannot lie, and you need not fear Satan and all his hosts. Jesus selected the best weapon. What was best for Him is best for you."
>
> - Charles Spurgeon -

- What is your greatest takeaway from today's study? _____
  _____
  _____
  _____

> "For we do not have a high priest who is unable to sympathize with our weaknesses, but one who in every respect has been tempted as we are, yet without sin."
>
> - Hebrews 4:15 -

- What does this verse mean to you? _____
  _____
  _____
  _____

# Spiritual Warfare - Day 2

- Read Ephesians 6. How can you apply each of these items to protect and defend your marriage?

  - BELT OF TRUTH (Armor connection point): _____

    _____

    _____

  - BREASTPLATE OF RIGHTEOUSNESS (Heart protector): _____

    _____

    _____

  - SANDALS-GOSPEL OF PEACE (Firmly planted): _____

    _____

    _____

  - SHIELD OF FAITH (Extinguishes flaming arrows): _____

    _____

    _____

  - HELMET OF SALVATION (Protects head/mind): _____

    _____

    _____

  - SWORD OF THE SPIRIT (Only offensive weapon): _____

    _____

    _____

- What hot topics in your marriage immediately cause unhealthy conflict when brought up?

  - _____  • _____  • _____

  - What tactics does Satan use to drive a wedge between you two? _____

    _____

    _____

  - Which spiritual armor piece (listed above) is your weakest link? _____

  - How could strengthening your weakest link help diffuse unhealthy conflict? _____

    _____

    _____

- Read James 1:13. What shift needs to occur in your heart and mind to realize Satan is the ultimate enemy in your relational conflict, not the other person or God? _____

_____

_____

- Read Ephesians 4:26-27. What opportunity does Paul speak of and why is it important? _____

_____

_____

- Read 1 Corinthians 7:5. Why is sexual deprivation a key tactic Satan uses to divide a marriage? _____

_____

_____

- Are you happy with the overall sexual health of your marriage? _____ Why or why not? _____

_____

_____

> "The mind and the emotions are the two areas where Satan most fiercely attacks believers. He wants to cloud our minds with false doctrine, false principles, and false information to mislead and confuse us. He also wants to confuse our emotions and thereby pervert our affection, morals, loyalties, goals, and commitments. He desires to snatch the Word of God from our minds and replace it with his own perverse ideas. He seeks to undermine pure living and replace it with immorality, greed, envy, hate, and every other vice. He wants us to laugh at sin rather than mourn over it, and to rationalize it rather than confess it and bring it to the Lord for forgiveness. He seduces us to become so accustomed to sin in us and around us that it no longer disturbs us."
>
> - John MacArthur -

- What is your greatest takeaway from today's study? _____

_____

_____

_____

> "For we do not wrestle against flesh and blood, but against the rulers, against the authorities, against the cosmic powers over this present darkness, against the spiritual forces of evil in the heavenly places."
>
> - Ephesians 6:12 -

- What does this verse mean to you? _____

_____

_____

_____

# Checkpoint 1

It is important to not get too far ahead of ourselves when navigating the wilderness and lose sight of how far we've come. Therefore, checkpoints have been created as opportunities to stop and reflect upon where we began this journey of faith and self-examination, what we've learned thus far by studying these specific topics, how God has transformed our hearts to this point, and what impact this study is having on our wives and children. In essence, these checkpoints are opportunities to establish spiritual markers which will act as trail markers on our wilderness journey, reminding us of God's provision and faithfulness to "restore the years the swarming locust has eaten" (Joel 2:25). Keep in mind, mountain-top perspective is most appreciated when we consider the valley from which we came and celebrate our progress made.

- Over the past 4-weeks, which Scripture passages you've studied have gripped your heart the most?

  - _____    - _____

  - _____    - _____

- Over the past 4-weeks, what has CONVICTED you most from each of the topics you've studied?

  - Theology: _____

    _____

  - Absolute Truth: _____

    _____

  - Faith: _____

    _____

  - Spiritual Warfare: _____

    _____

- Over the past 4-weeks, what has ENCOURAGED you most from each of the topics you've studied?

  - Theology: _____

    _____

  - Absolute Truth: _____

    _____

  - Faith: _____

    _____

  - Spiritual Warfare: _____

    _____

- How have you been INSPIRED to be a better husband to your wife over the past 4-weeks? _____
  _____
  _____
  _____

- How have you been INSPIRED to be a better father to your children over the past 4-weeks? _____
  _____
  _____
  _____

- How have you been INSPIRED to be a better man (in general) over the past 4-weeks? _____
  _____
  _____
  _____

> "Any training – physical, mental, or spiritual – is characterized at first by failure. We fail more often than we succeed. But if we persevere, we gradually see progress till we are succeeding more often than failing. This is true as we seek to put to death particular sins. At first it seems we are making no progress, so we become discouraged and think, what's the use?! I can never overcome that sin. That is exactly what Satan wants us to think. It is at this point that we must exercise perseverance. We keep wanting instant success, but holiness doesn't come that way. Our sinful habits are not broken overnight. Follow-through is required to make any change in our lives, and follow-through requires perseverance."
>
> - Jerry Bridges -

- Create one practical goal you plan to achieve moving forward and your inspiration (i.e. why?) for choosing it?
  - Theology: _____
    - Inspiration: _____
  - Absolute Truth: _____
    - Inspiration: _____
  - Faith: _____
    - Inspiration: _____
  - Spiritual Warfare: _____
    - Inspiration: _____

# Idolatry & Worship - Day 1

Idolatry and worship go hand in hand. They are impossible to separate because idolatry is fueled by false worship. The Bible warns that the more we devote our time, attention, energy and resources to anything or anyone other than Almighty God, the greater likelihood we fall into various forms of idolatry. The real question lies more in why we fail to worship God rather than what form our idolatry manifests itself. Therefore, the more intentional I address false worship, the healthier my spiritual life will be, inevitably causing a ripple effect upon my marriage/family. Idolatry is arguably the most destructive sin a man can encounter because it is interwoven throughout the fabric of his life. Only pure, reverent worship unto Jesus Christ can remedy our heart's epidemic toward serving false idols in our lives.

- What immediately comes to mind when you hear the word 'idolatry?' _____
  _____

- What immediately comes to mind when you hear the word 'worship?' _____
  _____

- How can Matthew 6:19-21 help you begin to understand God's perspective on worship and idolatry? _____
  _____
  _____
  _____

- Why is the 1st commandment (Deut. 6:5) "the greatest" as Jesus states in Matthew 22:36-38? _____
  _____
  _____

- Read Acts 2:42-47. Why is it important to worship together as a family with a corporate fellowship of Christ-followers? _____
  _____
  _____

- How can the body of Christ (the church) help encourage your worship and guard you from idolatry?
  - _____     · _____
  - _____     · _____

  - What stigmas against the church hinder you from embracing accountability? _____
    _____
    _____

- Read Luke 14:25-35. How does the cost of discipleship relate to worship and idolatry? _____

  _____

  _____

  - What impact does it have on your role as spiritual head of your family? _____

    _____

    _____

- What idols that your children struggle with can be traced back to your life and example?

  - _____    • _____    • _____

  - _____    • _____    • _____

  - Do you struggle owning that truth? _____ Why or why not? _____

    _____

    _____

    _____

    _____

> "O ye sons of men, think not that God is blind. He can perceive the idols in your hearts; He understands what be the secret things that your souls lust after; He searches your heart, He tries your reins; beware lest He find you sacrificing to strange gods, for His anger will smoke against you, and His jealousy will be stirred. O ye that worship not God, the God of Israel, who give Him not dominion over your whole soul, and live not to His honor, repent ye of your idolatry, seek mercy through the blood of Jesus, and provoke not the Lord to jealousy any more."
>
> - Charles Spurgeon -

- What is your greatest takeaway from today's study? _____

  _____

  _____

  _____

> "Little children, keep yourselves from idols."
>
> - 1 John 5:21 -

- What does this verse mean to you? _____

  _____

  _____

  _____

# Idolatry & Worship - Day 2

- How have the following idols caused division to some degree (big or small) in your life/marriage?

- Success/Vocation: _____

  _____

- Materialism: _____

  _____

- Sex/Lust: _____

  _____

- Power/Control: _____

  _____

- Financial Security: _____

  _____

- Comfort: _____

  _____

- Laziness: _____

  _____

- Knowledge: _____

  _____

- Praise/Adoration: _____

  _____

- Hobbies: _____

  _____

- Substance Abuse (any form): _____

  _____

- Anxiety/Stress: _____

  _____

- Anger: _____

  _____

- What wisdom can you glean from 1 Corinthians 10:1-22 to guard your heart from idolatry?

    - _____

    - _____

    - _____

- Read Psalm 115:1-8. If you become what you worship, how would you identify yourself?

    - _____        - _____

    - _____        - _____

    - Would your wife agree with your personal assessment? _____ Why or why not? _____
      _____
      _____

    - Do you consider yourself an idolater? _____ Why or why not? _____
      _____
      _____

> "Regardless of the reaction of others, one thing is certain: True worship and devotion will make our lives fragrant and will perfume the environment around us. Our homes, our churches, even our places of work will bear the sweet scent of our devotion. Most important, the Lord Jesus will be pleased. And ultimately that is all that really matters."
>
> - Nancy Leigh DeMoss -

- What is your greatest takeaway from today's study? _____
  _____
  _____
  _____

> "Do not be conformed to this world, but be transformed by the renewal of your mind, that by testing you may discern what is the will of God, what is good and acceptable and perfect."
>
> - Romans 12:2 -

- What does this verse mean to you? _____
  _____
  _____
  _____

# Rebellion - Day 1

It is difficult to examine a man's life without addressing the rebelliousness of his heart which wages war against the Spirit. Rebellion is simply a rejection of God's law which protects us from the wages of sin and death. It is the outward manifestation of sin in both thought and action. What many fail to realize is rejecting the perfect law of God rejects Christ. There is no separation between the inspired Word of God and the personhood of Jesus because they are interconnected. Therefore, in order to view sin entirely, we must acknowledge how rebelling against Scripture denies Christ. When I caught the eternal significance of John 1:1, God's Word became more than religious practice. It changed into a faith relationship, centered upon intimacy with Christ through His Word and the power of the Holy Spirit.

- When you reject someone or something, what are you communicating? _____
  _____
  _____

- What roles, responsibilities or expectations as a husband/father/brother/friend/etc. do you reject?

  - _____     - _____
  - _____     - _____
  - _____     - _____

- What topics in Scripture do you not agree with or aren't sure of?

  - ( _____ ) Why? _____
    _____

  - ( _____ ) Why? _____
    _____

- What topics in Scripture do you consider too vague or contradictory?

  - ( _____ ) Why? _____
    _____

  - ( _____ ) Why? _____
    _____

- How can John 1:1,14 change any rebellion in your heart regarding what the Bible teaches? _____
  _____
  _____
  _____

- What does it mean to be spiritually blind to your own blindness? _____
  _____
  _____

- Read Hebrews 3:7-19. What is the ultimate danger of spiritual rebellion? _____
  _____
  _____

- How have you hardened your heart toward the Lord? _____
  _____
  _____

- What fears/insecurities hinder you from having an accountability partner in your life? _____
  _____
  _____

- Who could you trust to start an accountability relationship with today? _____

> "When individuals rebel against God, they don't achieve freedom. They fall into bondage, because rebellion is sin, and sin is a tyrant. On the other hand, when men and women submit to God, becoming his slaves, they become truly free. They achieve the ability fully to become the special, unique beings that God created them to be."
>
> - James Montgomery Boice -

- What is your greatest takeaway from today's study? _____
  _____
  _____
  _____

> "To the Lord our God belong mercy and forgiveness, for we have rebelled against him and have not obeyed the voice of the LORD our God by walking in his laws, which he set before us by his servants the prophets."
>
> - Daniel 9:9-10 -

- What does this verse mean to you? _____
  _____
  _____
  _____

# Rebellion ~ Day 2

- What sinful, behavioral patterns does the Lord need to sift from your heart in moments of conflict?

  - _____

  - _____

  - _____

- What does Matthew 12:36 reveal about rebellion through the words you speak? _____
  _____
  _____

- Within marriage, rebellion can often be identified when a wife holds her husband accountable. How do you typically REACT to your wife's content (what she is saying) and her presentation (how she is saying it)?

  - Content: _____
    _____
    _____

  - Presentation: _____
    _____
    _____

- Humility in marriage is evident when a man can sift truth from "lost in translation" static his wife may communicate, which distracts true growth and heart change (i.e. fighting over meaningless details rather than the deeper issue at hand). Give an example how you've failed and gained victory in this area.

  - Example of Failure: _____
    _____
    _____
    _____
    _____

  - Example of Victory: _____
    _____
    _____
    _____
    _____

- What rebellious part of your upbringing do you remember most? What happened? _____
  _____
  _____

  - What did you learn as a result? _____
    _____
    _____

- What similarities do you share with the rebellion developing in your children?

  - _____     - _____

  - _____     - _____

  - How can you help break these patterns? _____
    _____

  - What rebellion do you pray your children avoid most? _____ Why? _____
    _____

> "Sin is a moral problem. It is about my rebellion against God and my quest to have for myself the glory that is due Him. Sin is not first about the breaking of an abstract set of rules. Sin is first and foremost about breaking relationship with God, and because I have broken this relationship, it is then easy and natural to rebel against God's rules."
>
> - Paul David Tripp -

- What is your greatest takeaway from today's study? _____
  _____
  _____
  _____

> "Why will you still be struck down? Why will you continue to rebel?
> The whole head is sick, and the whole heart faint."
>
> - Isaiah 1:5 -

- What does this verse mean to you? _____
  _____
  _____
  _____

# Love of Self - Day 1

Our lives are a battle between flesh and spirit, and our heart's devotion is at the crux of that war. Truthfully, we love ourselves more than God, for we seek to fulfill our desires in virtually every decision we make. In many ways, our sinful DNA is programmed to think, "Me first!" Therefore, we must quiet our minds and intentionally listen for God's voice above the static and confusion of life. Ashamedly, I'm guilty of loving myself far more than the Lord on a daily basis. However, He is long-suffering despite my attempts to satisfy selfish desires before obeying Him. That is why His grace is so amazing and His love everlasting, because He chose to save me knowing full well how wretched I truly am. How then can I love myself more than Him and take for granted the priceless sacrifice He made on my behalf?

- Read Romans 7:14-20. How do you relate to the struggle Paul describes? _____
_____
_____

- How does 2 Corinthians 10:3-4 transform your approach to battling the flesh? _____
_____
_____

- In what ways have you communicated to your wife, "I am more important than you!"

  - _____

  - _____

  - Which behavior is most convicting to you? _____ Why? _____
  _____
  _____

- Even when you serve your wife, selfish motives can drive your actions behind the scenes. What are you guilty of discreetly manipulating in order to distort/twist her response in your favor?

  - I give: _____     To get: _____
  - I give: _____     To get: _____
  - I give: _____     To get: _____
  - I give: _____     To get: _____

- How can dying to self result in humility rather than guilt, shame and regret? _____
_____
_____

- Read Romans 7:7-25. What stands out to you most from this passage? _____
_____
_____

- If love of self is the true root of all evil, what "surface" sin issues monopolize your time and attention, distracting you from attacking the core problem?

  - _____        - _____

  - _____        - _____

- Why is it so easy for a man to compartmentalize his sin as affecting only himself and not others? _____
_____
_____
_____

> "The essence of man's sin, the sum of his moral depravity, is to love himself supremely; to seek himself finally and exclusively; to make self, in one shape or another, the center to which all his busy thoughts, anxious cares and diligent pursuits, constantly tend. Self-love is the most active and reigning principle in fallen nature! SELF is the great idol which mankind is naturally disposed to worship."
>
> - John Angell James -
>
> "In our proud love affair with ourselves we pour contempt, whether we know it or not, on the worth of God's glory. As our pride pours contempt upon God's glory, His righteousness obliges Him to pour wrath upon our pride."
>
> - John Piper -

- What is your greatest takeaway from today's study? _____
_____
_____
_____

> "Let each of you look not only to his own interests, but also to the interests of others."
> - Philippians 2:4 -

- What does this verse mean to you? _____
_____
_____
_____

# Love of Self - Day 2

- Read Galatians 5:16-17. What is the Holy Spirit's role concerning your flesh? _____

  _____

  _____

- Read Galatians 5:19-21. Which works of the flesh are most evident in your life?

  - _____  • _____  • _____  • _____

  - What is the common thread binding these together? _____

    _____

    _____

- When are you most prone to justify your sin rather than accept responsibility for it and change? _____

  _____

  _____

- Give a recent example how this played out in your marriage. _____

  _____

  _____

- Read James 1:12-15. Give an example when temptation led to sin and inevitably death, thus affecting your marriage because of selfish desire.

  - What happened? _____

    _____

    _____

    _____

  - How did God redeem you through it? _____

    _____

    _____

    _____

- Read Philippians 2:3. What three things does Paul encourage you to avoid?

  - _____  • _____  • _____

  - Describe one way you can begin counting others more significant than yourself. _____

    _____

    _____

- How have you communicated to your children, "I am more important than you?"

  - _____

  - _____

  - _____

- Give an example how your father modeled love (selfish or selfless) toward your mother. _____
  _____
  _____
  _____

- Read Ephesians 5:28-30. How does Paul put love of self into perspective within marriage? _____
  _____
  _____
  _____

> "Too many Christians never see that self-love comes out of a culture that prizes the individual over the community and then reads that basic principle into the pages of Scripture. The Bible, however, rightly understood, asks the question, "Why are you so concerned about yourself?" Furthermore, it indicates that our culture's proposed cure – increased self-love – is actually the disease. If we fail to recognize the reality and depth of our sin problem, God will become less important, and people will become more important."
>
> - Edward Welch -

- What is your greatest takeaway from today's study? _____
  _____
  _____
  _____

> "Let another praise you, and not your own mouth; a stranger, and not your own lips."
> - Proverbs 27:2 -

- What does this verse mean to you? _____
  _____
  _____
  _____

# Hypocrisy - Day 1

Hypocrisy is the epitome of living contrary to the absolute truth of God's Word. A hypocrite presents himself publicly as if he were living unto righteousness, but privately exalts himself above God by the decisions he makes to serve himself first. Hypocrisy is dependent upon deceit to conceal the true character of a man's heart, which will undermine his marriage and devalue the integrity of his word if he allows. The key is recognizing how love of self impacts decision-making. I know this because I was once spiritually blind to my own blindness and duped myself into thinking I could live for Christ while satisfying my selfish desires. I learned God's warning the hard way that a man cannot serve two masters, and a spiritual split-personality is a tried and true recipe for self-destruction and heartache.

- What does a hypocritical person look like (what words come to mind)?

  - _____  - _____  - _____  - _____

- Do you consider yourself a hypocrite? _____ Why or why not? _____
  _____
  _____

- Would your wife agree with you? _____ Why or why not? _____
  _____
  _____

- Why do you believe Jesus passionately rebuked hypocrisy more than any other sin issue? _____
  _____
  _____

- Read Galatians 5:19-21. Which sins of hypocrisy are you guilty of? How so?

  - Sin: _____ How? _____
    _____

  - Sin: _____ How? _____
    _____

  - Sin: _____ How? _____
    _____

- Give an example how you were on the receiving end of someone else's hypocrisy. _____
  _____
  _____

- Read Galatians 5:22-23. Which fruits of the spirit do you struggle with most in your marriage?

  - #1 Fruit: _____ Why? _____
    _____

  - #2 Fruit: _____ Why? _____
    _____

  - #3 Fruit: _____ Why? _____
    _____

- Read 1 John 4:20. How have you allowed hate to take root in your heart?

  - With Whom? _____ How? _____
    _____

  - With Whom? _____ How? _____
    _____

> "Whenever the true message of the cross is abolished, the anger of hypocrites and heretics eases... and all things are in peace. This is a sure token that the devil is guarding the entry of that house, and that the pure doctrine of God's Word has been taken away. The church, then, is in the BEST state when Satan assaileth it on every side...both with subtle sleights, and outright violence. And (likewise) it is in the WORST state, when it is most at peace!"
>
> - Martin Luther -

- What is your greatest takeaway from today's study? _____
  _____
  _____
  _____

> "How can you say to your brother, 'Brother, let me take out the speck that is in your eye,' when you yourself do not see the log that is in your own eye? You hypocrite, first take the log out of your own eye, and then you will see clearly to take out the speck that is in your brother's eye."
>
> - Luke 6:42 -

- What does this verse mean to you? _____
  _____
  _____
  _____

# Hypocrisy - Day 2

- Read Matthew 23:1-36. Summarize each of the 7 woes Jesus passionately rebuked.

  1. _____
     _____

  2. _____
     _____

  3. _____
     _____

  4. _____
     _____

  5. _____
     _____

  6. _____
     _____

  7. _____
     _____

- Which "woe" do you identify with most? __#__ Why? _____
  _____
  _____

- Read Matthew 6:1-18. How can you guard your marriage and avoid hypocrisy with these behaviors?

  - Giving: _____
    _____

  - Fasting: _____
    _____

  - Praying: _____
    _____

- Why is it critical YOU model morality and integrity as spiritual leader of your home? _____
  _____
  _____

- What are potential dangers of allowing hypocrisy to take root in your professional workplace?

  - _____

  - _____

- Read Galatians 2:11-14. What was the hypocrisy Paul confronted Peter about? _____
  _____
  _____

- How have you led your wife/children astray by a hypocritical decision you have made?

  - What happened? _____
    _____

  - How were you held accountable? _____
    _____

  - What were the consequences of your actions? _____
    _____

> "Children are very quick observers, very quick in seeing through some kinds of hypocrisy,
> very quick in finding out what you really think and feel, very quick in adopting all your ways
> and opinions. You will often discover that, as the father is, so is the son."
>
> - J.C. Ryle -
>
> "It is the mark of a hypocrite to be a Christian everywhere but home."
>
> - Robert Murray McCheyne -

- What is your greatest takeaway from today's study? _____
  _____
  _____
  _____

> "Why do you call me 'Lord, Lord,' and not do what I tell you?"
>
> - Luke 6:46 -

- What does this verse mean to you? _____
  _____
  _____
  _____

# Checkpoint 2

It is important to not get too far ahead of ourselves when navigating the wilderness and lose sight of how far we've come. Therefore, checkpoints have been created as opportunities to stop and reflect upon where we began this journey of faith and self-examination, what we've learned thus far by studying these specific topics, how God has transformed our hearts to this point, and what impact this study is having on our wives and children. In essence, these checkpoints are opportunities to establish spiritual markers which will act as trail markers on our wilderness journey, reminding us of God's provision and faithfulness to "restore the years the swarming locust has eaten" (Joel 2:25). Keep in mind, mountain-top perspective is most appreciated when we consider the valley from which we came and celebrate our progress made.

- Over the past 4-weeks, which Scripture passages you've studied have gripped your heart the most?

  - _____     - _____

  - _____     - _____

- Over the past 4-weeks, what has CONVICTED you most from each of the topics you've studied?

  - Idolatry & Worship: _____
    _____

  - Rebellion: _____
    _____

  - Love of Self: _____
    _____

  - Hypocrisy: _____
    _____

- Over the past 4-weeks, what has ENCOURAGED you most from each of the topics you've studied?

  - Idolatry & Worship: _____
    _____

  - Rebellion: _____
    _____

  - Love of Self: _____
    _____

  - Hypocrisy: _____
    _____

- How have you been INSPIRED to be a better husband to your wife over the past 4-weeks? _____

  _____

  _____

  _____

- How have you been INSPIRED to be a better father to your children over the past 4-weeks? _____

  _____

  _____

  _____

- How have you been INSPIRED to be a better man (in general) over the past 4-weeks? _____

  _____

  _____

  _____

> "I wish that saints would cling to Christ half as earnestly as sinners cling to the devil.
> If we were as willing to suffer for God as some are willing to suffer for their lusts,
> what perseverance and zeal would be seen on all sides!"
>
> - Charles Spurgeon -
>
> "We all have a cross to carry. But it's a cross that kills our sins, smashes our idols,
> and teaches us the folly of self-reliance. It's a cross that says I'll do anything to follow Jesus,
> not a cross that says I have to do everything for Jesus."
>
> - Kevin DeYoung -

- Create one practical goal per topic you plan to achieve moving forward and your inspiration for choosing it.

  - Idolatry & Worship: _____

    - Inspiration: _____

  - Rebellion: _____

    - Inspiration: _____

  - Love of Self: _____

    - Inspiration: _____

  - Hypocrisy: _____

    - Inspiration: _____

# Identity - Day 1

Past experiences shape who we are today, even though every man wishes he could take back things he's ashamed of. However, we are not defined by our past if we're saved by grace through faith in Jesus. Every born-again Christian has a new identity in Christ and been granted supernatural power through the indwelling power of the Holy Spirit to turn away from sin and temptation. The challenge is that the Spirit is willing but the flesh is weak. I have learned my true identity is found in Jesus Christ, but that does not disregard my past and the consequences of sin. Who I was and who I am today are forever intertwined. Therefore, I can pursue positive change in my thoughts and behavior because I am not bound by my past or my sinful flesh, for Christ is my identity regardless whether I fall again.

- When you introduce yourself to someone, what information do you typically share?

    - _____  • _____  • _____

    - Do any traits you've listed identify you as a man of faith? _____ If not, why? _____
    _____

- How would you define what a Christian looks like? What identity traits come to mind?

    - _____  • _____  • _____

    - _____  • _____  • _____

    - Circle the traits which best describe YOU and draw an "X" through the ones that don't.

    - Would your wife agree with your assessment? _____ Why or why not? _____
    _____
    _____

- Read Jeremiah 1:5, 29:11. What do these verses reveal about God's relationship to you? _____
_____
_____

- Read Genesis 1:27. Since you are created in God's image, what is your purpose in life? _____
_____
_____

- Read 1 Corinthians 7:17-24. Knowing "you were bought with a price," what impact does this have on your personal faith journey? _____
_____
_____

- Do you ever struggle understanding why you still sin even though you are saved? _____ Why or why not?

  _____
  _____
  _____

- Read Galatians 2:20. Why is this truth encouraging when you feel enslaved to your flesh? _____

  _____
  _____
  _____

- For change to be genuine and believable, what specific behaviors need to be evident?

  • _____    • _____    • _____

    - What role does consistency play in gaining trust? _____

      _____
      _____

> "We must understand how to separate our "who" from our "do." What we do does not gain us God's affection. Who we are by virtue of His unconditional love constrains us through the power of our gratitude to obey Him. If we ever invert these relationships (as is the instinctive, natural impulse of all humanity) by assuming that who we are before God is a consequence of what we do for Him, then we make God's love conditional and our security questionable."
>
> - Bryan Chapell -

- What is your greatest takeaway from today's study? _____

  _____
  _____
  _____

> "Therefore, if anyone is in Christ, he is a new creation.
> The old has passed away; behold, the new has come."
>
> - 2 Corinthians 5:17 -

- What does this verse mean to you? _____

  _____
  _____
  _____

# Identity - Day 2

- What words come to mind when you reflect upon who you were/are at the following life stages?

| BEFORE MARRIAGE | FIRST MARRIED | PRESENT DAY |
|---|---|---|
| • _____ | • _____ | • _____ |
| • _____ | • _____ | • _____ |
| • _____ | • _____ | • _____ |

- What sinful actions/behavior/attitudes of your past do you feel your wife struggles letting go of?

  - _____

  - _____

  - _____

  - Do you understand why she struggles? _____ Why or why not? _____
    _____
    _____

- In marriage, some hold onto the past as a security blanket because change is difficult to trust and perhaps accepting change in your spouse forces you to deal with the plank in your own eye. Therefore, what identity traits your wife possesses are you willing to surrender to God by faith for reconciliation to begin in your marriage, and what do you pray she surrenders concerning you?

| I WILL SURRENDER | I PRAY SHE SURRENDERS |
|---|---|
| • _____ | • _____ |
| • _____ | • _____ |
| • _____ | • _____ |

- Read Matthew 18:21-22. How are you guilty of holding your wife's past sins against her?

  - _____

  - _____

- Read Isaiah 43:25. How can you apply this verse to your marriage? _____
  _____
  _____

- How are you identifying yourself with past sins which God has already forgiven? _____

  _____

  _____

- What are potential dangers of not forgiving yourself for sins you've committed?

  - _____   - _____

  - _____   - _____

  - CIRCLE the answer you're most struggling with currently.

- How can your wife help affirm and encourage you to embrace your identity in Christ?

  - _____

  - _____

  - _____

> "If you are not feeding your soul on the realities of the presence, promises, and provisions of Christ, you will ask the people, situations, and things around you to be the messiah that they can never be. If you are not attaching your identity to the unshakable love of your Savior, you will ask the things in your life to be your Savior, and it will never happen. If you are not requiring yourself to get your deepest sense of well-being vertically, you will shop for it horizontally, and you will always come up empty. If you are not resting in the one true gospel, preaching it to yourself over and over again, you will look to another gospel to meet the needs of your unsettled heart."
>
> - Paul David Tripp -

- What is your greatest takeaway from today's study? _____

  _____

  _____

  _____

> "For we are his workmanship, created in Christ Jesus for good works, which God prepared beforehand, that we should walk in them."
>
> - Ephesians 2:10 -

- What does this verse mean to you? _____

  _____

  _____

  _____

# Attitudes - Day 1

Attitudes reflect the heart's condition. Whether good or bad, we communicate more than we realize when we allow fleshly attitudes to trump the divine leading of the Spirit at work in us. God is not honored when we're led by emotions rather than His Word, and those emotions can wreak havoc on our marriages because they feel natural. I cannot think of another issue my wife consistently holds me accountable for more than poor attitudes. Despite my best efforts, I still fall prey to what comes natural (sin) rather than what I know to be true in God's Word. I have learned the easiest way to measure whether I am growing in my faith is to observe the attitudes I display toward my wife and children, and whether they reflect the heart of Christ or my twisted flesh which elevates love of self.

- Read Numbers 11. What wisdom can you glean from the Israelites' negative attitude toward God?

    - What was their desire? _____

    - Why did they complain? _____

    - What did their complaining reveal about God? _____

    - How did God respond? _____

    - What lesson can you apply from their example? _____
    _____

- What positive attitudes does your wife often express when she is pleased with you?

    - _____     - _____

    - _____     - _____

- What negative attitudes does your wife convey during moments of conflict with you?

    - _____     - _____

    - _____     - _____

- Read Daniel 4:4-37. Perspective comes when we begin to see our lives from God's view. How can you relate to Daniel's words where God has revealed Himself to you in a supernatural way? _____
_____
_____

    - Give an example where God has restored you. _____
    _____
    _____

- What fears hold you back from humbling yourself as spiritual leader of your home?

- _____     • _____

- _____     • _____

  - Which fear does your wife hold you accountable to most? _____
    Why? _____

    _____

- What attitudes have been passed onto your children through your example?

|  POSITIVE ATTITUDES  |  NEGATIVE ATTITUDES  |
| --- | --- |
| • _____ | • _____ |
| • _____ | • _____ |
| • _____ | • _____ |
| • _____ | • _____ |

> "An unthankful and complaining spirit is an abiding sin against God, and a cause of almost continual unhappiness; and yet how common such a spirit is. How prone we seem to be to forget the good that life knows, and remember and brood over its evil – to forget its joys, and think only of its sorrows – to forget thankfulness, and remember only to complain."
>
> - John Broadus -

- What is your greatest takeaway from today's study? _____

_____

_____

_____

> "Finally, brothers, whatever is true, whatever is honorable, whatever is just, whatever is pure, whatever is lovely, whatever is commendable, if there is any excellence, if there is anything worthy of praise, think about these things."
>
> - Philippians 4:8 -

- What does this verse mean to you? _____

_____

_____

_____

# Attitudes ~ Day 2

- How can you PUT OFF the following negative attitudes your wife endures from you?

  - Complaining: _____
  - Criticizing: _____
  - Demeaning: _____
  - Ignoring: _____
  - Discrediting: _____
  - Minimizing: _____
  - Lack of Interest: _____
  - Sarcasm: _____
  - Know-It-All: _____
  - Sexual Innuendos: _____

- How can you PUT ON the following positive attitudes your wife would benefit from if you applied?

  - Thankfulness: _____
  - Contentment: _____
  - Love: _____
  - Appreciation: _____
  - Understanding: _____
  - Compassion: _____
  - Intentionality: _____
  - Humility: _____
  - Empathy: _____

- What does Romans 12:2 look like in your marriage at this moment? How have you conformed to the world's pattern? _____

_____

_____

- What does Romans 8:31-39 reveal about God's attitude toward His children? _____
  _____
  _____

- What convicts you about this passage as you apply it to your family? _____
  _____
  _____

- What practical changes can you make to affirm/encourage those under your spiritual leadership?

| TOWARD MY WIFE | TOWARD MY CHILDREN |
| --- | --- |
| • _____ | • _____ |
| • _____ | • _____ |
| • _____ | • _____ |
| • _____ | • _____ |

- What is the biggest risk of not making changes? _____
  _____

> "Spiritual strongholds begin with a thought. One thought becomes a consideration.
> A consideration develops into an attitude, which leads then to action. Action repeated becomes
> a habit, and a habit establishes a "power base for the enemy," that is, a stronghold."
>
> - Elisabeth Elliot -

- What is your greatest takeaway from today's study? _____
  _____
  _____
  _____

> "For to set the mind on the flesh is death, but to set the mind on the Spirit is life and peace. For the
> mind that is set on the flesh is hostile to God, for it does not submit to God's law; indeed, it cannot."
>
> - Romans 8:6-7 -

- What does this verse mean to you? _____
  _____
  _____
  _____

# Assumptions & Expectations – Day 1

Nothing will destroy a marriage from the inside-out more than assumptions and expectations. They are a thorn in the flesh for most couples because we assume based on the amount of time spent together, we know what each other is thinking and feeling. Similarly, expectations wreak havoc because they place unnecessary pressure upon our wives due to selfish motives and intent. I have witnessed the destructive nature and widespread effect they have on my wife. For when I reflect upon my love of self, roots of assumptions and expectations can be identified playing a direct or indirect role in my ultimate demise. In other words, when I assume I know something, I often realize I don't; and when I begin to formulate expectations, disappointment and frustration typically result and conflict arises.

- What is lacking in your marriage that, if remedied, would potentially "fix" your marriage?

  - _____

  - _____

  - _____

- What do you assume your wife wishes she could change about you to make her happy?

  - _____

  - _____

  - _____

- What does Hebrews 10:26-27 caution you to expect if you, as a man of God, continue to live in sin? _____
  _____
  _____

  - How does this impact how you love and protect your wife when battling temptations? _____
    _____
    _____

- What does Proverbs 18:13 teach about assumptions? _____
  _____

- Read 1 Corinthians 10:12. In what areas of your life do you assume you're well-guarded?

  - _____  · _____  · _____

  - How could Satan use your self-confidence against you? _____
    _____

- Read Luke 6:35. How can you "expect nothing in return" from your enemies?

  - _____     - _____

  - _____     - _____

- What are practical rewards for "expecting nothing in return" from your enemies?

  - _____     - _____

  - _____     - _____

- Men typically place unrealistic expectations on their wives because of preconceived ideas they hold as mandatory prior to getting married. What expectations are you continuing to hold over your wife?

  - _____

  - _____

  - What has been the collateral damage of holding your ground all these years? _____
    _____

> "I commend solitude to any of you who are seeking salvation, first, that you may study well your case as in the sight of God. Few men truly know themselves as they really are. Most people have seen themselves in a looking-glass, but there is another looking-glass, which gives true reflections, into which few men look. To study one's self in the light of God's Word, and carefully to go over one's condition, examining both the inward and the outward sins, and using all the tests which are given us in the Scriptures, would be a very healthy exercise; but how very few care to go through it!"
>
> - Charles Spurgeon -

- What is your greatest takeaway from today's study? _____
  _____
  _____
  _____

> "The desire of the righteous ends only in good, the expectation of the wicked in wrath."
> - Proverbs 11:23 -

- What does this verse mean to you? _____
  _____
  _____
  _____

# Assumptions & Expectations - Day 2

- What are dangers of living with a surface understanding of Scripture rather than reading it daily?

    - _____  •  _____  •  _____

- Read Ephesians 5:22-33. What shift in understanding needs to take place in your heart regarding what true, Biblical submission looks like? _____

  _____

  _____

- When your wife submits to your authority as head, what does that mean?

    - What is she assuming? _____

      _____

    - What is she expecting? _____

      _____

    - What is her greatest fear? _____

      _____

    - How is her submission an honor to you? _____

      _____

    - Do you realize her submission to your marital role has nothing to do with you? _____ Why or why not? _____

      _____

    - Do you realize God expects the same level of submission from you? _____ Why or why not?

      _____

      _____

- What excuses allow your flesh to assume a posture of laziness as spiritual leader of your home?

    - _____  •  _____  •  _____

    - A heart consumed by spiritual laziness can expect what in return? _____

      _____

    - How does the Bible identify someone who is lazy? _____

      _____

- How does your wife typically react/respond when you assume you know what she's thinking? _____

  _____

  _____

  - How can you guard against this? _____

    _____

    _____

- What does God expect from you as a follower of Christ?

  🔥 • _____ • _____ • _____

  • _____ • _____ • _____

  - CIRCLE the expectations you're weakest in.

- What are potential dangers of unmet and unrealistic expectations toward your family?

  • _____

  • _____

  • _____

> "Sin plays havoc with our spiritual vision. Although we are able to see the sin of others with specificity and clarity, we tend to be blind to our own. And the most dangerous aspect of this already dangerous condition is that spiritually blind people tend to be blind to their blindness."
>
> - Paul David Tripp -

- What is your greatest takeaway from today's study? _____

  _____

  _____

  _____

> "You also must be ready, for the Son of Man is coming at an hour you do not expect."
> - Luke 12:40 -

- What does this verse mean to you? _____

  _____

  _____

  _____

# Entitlement - Day 1

Have you ever said something that began with the words, "I deserve...?" I believe at some point we all have said it if not thought it. Entitlement is a discreet issue which manifests itself in our flesh. Whether justifiable or not, we are ultimately entitled to nothing because God is the giver of all blessings for His honor and glory, not ours. When we realize life is not about our happiness and begin to embrace opportunities God gives us to grow spiritually, we shift from worldly-influenced, temporary happiness to eternal fulfillment serving the Lord. The more entitled I feel, the further apart I drift from God because I elevate myself above Him to fulfill my desires and supplant His supreme authority with idolatry. My happiness is best served being solely dependent upon His sovereign will, not mine.

- If entitlement states a claim to something, what do you believe you're "entitled to" in marriage?

  - _____  • _____  • _____

  - _____  • _____  • _____

- When you do not receive the respect you "deserve," how do you react and how should you respond?

  - My typical reaction: _____

  - How I should respond: _____

  - Why is responding a wiser choice than reacting? _____
  _____

- Read Isaiah 53:3-12. In contrast to Jesus, how does Scripture convict you regarding entitlement?

  - _____

  - _____

  - _____

- Considering Christ's sacrifice for His bride, what is your wife most entitled to and deserving of from you? Give examples how you can communicate that to her.

  - (                         ) How: _____
  _____

  - (                         ) How: _____
  _____

  - (                         ) How: _____
  _____

- Read 1 Timothy 1:15-16. How can this truth shape your perspective as a servant-leader? _____
_____
_____

- What does John 3:30 mean to you concerning entitlement? _____
_____
_____

- In what specific areas of your life do you need to increase and decrease for the sake of Christ?

| INCREASE (EMBRACE) | DECREASE (REJECT) |
|---|---|
| • _____ | • _____ |
| • _____ | • _____ |
| • _____ | • _____ |
| • _____ | • _____ |

> "Human beings, being what they are, somehow feel entitled to question the reasons for everything that happens to them. In many instances life itself becomes a continual criticism and dissection of one's circumstances and acquaintances.
> We look for someone or something on which to pin the blame for our misfortunes.
> We are often quick to forget our blessings, slow to forget our misfortunes."
>
> - Phillip Keller -

- What is your greatest takeaway from today's study? _____
_____
_____
_____

> "Such is the confidence that we have through Christ toward God. Not that we are sufficient in ourselves to claim anything as coming from us, but our sufficiency is from God."
>
> - 2 Corinthians 3:4-5 -

- What does this verse mean to you? _____
_____
_____
_____

# Entitlement - Day 2

- Read Matthew 6:19-21. What things of this world tempt your flesh, falsely promising entitlement, happiness and fulfillment?

  - _____   • _____   • _____   • _____

  - _____   • _____   • _____   • _____

    - Are your answers more physical/material or emotional/spiritual? _____

    - What other patterns or similarities can be found in your answers? _____
    _____

- Read Proverbs 5:20-21. What role does entitlement play in seeking fulfillment outside of marriage? _____
_____
_____

- Considering lustful temptations, what justifications/excuses do you use when your sexual desires are not being met by your wife and you pursue fulfillment elsewhere (i.e. mental/virtual/physical)?

  - _____   • _____

  - _____   • _____

    - What are dangers of mental lust (wandering eyes)? _____
    _____

    - What are dangers of virtual lust (cyber/social media)? _____
    _____

    - What are dangers of self-satisfaction (masturbation)? _____
    _____

    - Do you believe adultery of the mind is equally accountable to physical adultery? _____
    Why or why not? _____
    _____

- Read Psalm 94:2. How is pride a precursor to entitlement? _____
_____

  - Give an example how you've personally learned this lesson. _____
  _____
  _____

- Is it wrong to feel entitled to respect from your wife/children? _____ Why or why not? _____
  _____
  _____

🔥
  - Do you believe respect must be given or earned? _____ What is the difference? _____
    _____
    _____

  - What dangers exist when you demand respect? _____
    _____
    _____

- Looking back, to what degree (positive/negative) was entitlement modeled for you by your parents?

🔥
  - Father: _____
    _____

  - Mother: _____
    _____

> "If God was the owner, I was the manager. I needed to adopt a steward's mentality toward the assets He had entrusted – not given – to me. A steward manages assets for the owner's benefit. The steward carries no sense of entitlement to the assets he manages. It's his job to find out what the owner wants done with his assets, then carry out his will."
>
> - Randy Alcorn -

- What is your greatest takeaway from today's study? _____
  _____
  _____
  _____

> "But godliness with contentment is great gain, for we brought nothing into the world, and we cannot take anything out of the world."
>
> - 1 Timothy 6:6-7 -

- What does this verse mean to you? _____
  _____
  _____
  _____

# Checkpoint 3

It is important to not get too far ahead of ourselves when navigating the wilderness and lose sight of how far we've come. Therefore, checkpoints have been created as opportunities to stop and reflect upon where we began this journey of faith and self-examination, what we've learned thus far by studying these specific topics, how God has transformed our hearts to this point, and what impact this study is having on our wives and children. In essence, these checkpoints are opportunities to establish spiritual markers which will act as trail markers on our wilderness journey, reminding us of God's provision and faithfulness to "restore the years the swarming locust has eaten" (Joel 2:25). Keep in mind, mountain-top perspective is most appreciated when we consider the valley from which we came and celebrate our progress made.

- Over the past 4-weeks, which Scripture passages you've studied have gripped your heart the most?

  - _____      - _____
  - _____      - _____

- Over the past 4-weeks, what has CONVICTED you most from each of the topics you've studied?

  - Identity: _____
    _____

  - Attitudes: _____
    _____

  - Assumptions & Expectations: _____
    _____

  - Entitlement: _____
    _____

- Over the past 4-weeks, what has ENCOURAGED you most from each of the topics you've studied?

  - Identity: _____
    _____

  - Attitudes: _____
    _____

  - Assumptions & Expectations: _____
    _____

  - Entitlement: _____
    _____

- How have you been INSPIRED to be a better husband to your wife over the past 4-weeks? _____

  _____

  _____

  _____

- How have you been INSPIRED to be a better father to your children over the past 4-weeks? _____

  _____

  _____

  _____

- How have you been INSPIRED to be a better man (in general) over the past 4-weeks? _____

  _____

  _____

  _____

> "Our wills must be broken to His will. To be broken is the beginning of revival.
> It is painful, it is humiliating, it is the only way. The Lord Jesus cannot live in us fully
> and reveal Himself through us until the proud self within us is broken.
> This simply means that the hard unyielding self, which justifies itself, wants its own way,
> stands up for its rights, and seeks its own glory, at last bows its head to God's will,
> admits it's wrong, gives up its own way to Jesus, surrenders its rights
> and discards its own glory – that the Lord Jesus might have all and be all.
> In other words, it is dying to self and self-attitudes."
>
> - Roy Hession -

- Create one practical goal per topic you plan to achieve moving forward and your inspiration for choosing it.

  - Identity: _____

    - Inspiration: _____

  - Attitudes: _____

    - Inspiration: _____

  - Assumptions & Expectations: _____

    - Inspiration: _____

  - Entitlement: _____

    - Inspiration: _____

# Self-Righteousness - Day 1

Self-righteousness is the epitome of self-centered arrogance. It elevates oneself as morally superior to others. However, Scripture is full of stern warnings Jesus made toward those who cast their lot exalting self-recognition rather than the righteousness of God. Matthew 23 is a tutorial on avoiding self-righteous behavior, which easily morphs into legalistic tendencies if we're living for ourselves under the false pretense of serving God. In other words, we cannot identify ourselves as Christians and publicly portray a righteous image while privately exalting ourselves. Jesus rebuked the scribes and pharisees because they positioned themselves above others and ultimately God, and we are wise to learn from their mistakes so as not to think more highly of ourselves than we ought. Pride goes before a fall.

- Do you see yourself as self-righteous? _____ Why or why not? _____

  _____

  _____

- What words characterize/describe what a self-righteous man looks like?

  - _____   • _____   • _____

  - _____   • _____   • _____

  - Which two words do you identify with most? _____ & _____

- Why is Ephesians 2:8-10 foundational to understanding the dangers of self-righteousness? _____

  _____

  _____

- Why is it wise to avoid comparing yourself with others? _____

  _____

  _____

- Read Luke 18:9-14. In what ways do you play the role of pharisee in your life?

  - At Home: _____

  - At Church: _____

  - At Work: _____

- What fears prevent you from asking your wife to point out any self-righteousness she sees in you?

  - _____

  - _____

- If asked for examples of your self-righteousness, how do you perceive your family would answer?

FROM MY WIFE'S PERSPECTIVE          FROM MY KID'S PERSPECTIVE

- _____          - _____

- _____          - _____

- _____          - _____

- How are you taking credit for the good in your life rather than praising God for what He has done?

- _____

- _____

- _____

> "The very nature of self-righteousness is to justify self and condemn others. In so doing people play God, because they judge themselves on the basis of their own standards and wisdom. Self-righteousness is the worst of sins because it is unbelief. It trusts in self rather than God. It trusts in self to determine what is right and wrong and to determine who does what is right or wrong. Self-righteousness claims to be both lawgiver and judge, prerogatives that belong only to the Lord."
>
> - John MacArthur -

- What is your greatest takeaway from today's study? _____

_____

_____

_____

> "Not everyone who says to me, 'Lord, Lord,' will enter the kingdom of heaven, but the one who does the will of my Father who is in heaven. On that day many will say to me, 'Lord, Lord, did we not prophesy in your name, and cast out demons in your name, and do many mighty works in your name?' And then will I declare to them, 'I never knew you; depart from me, you workers of lawlessness.'"
>
> - Matthew 7:21-23 -

- What does this verse mean to you? _____

_____

_____

_____

# Self-Righteousness ~ Day 2

- Read 1 Timothy 1:12-17 and reflect upon the perspective you've learned from being self-righteous.

  - Who were you formerly? _____

    _____

  - How did you glorify yourself as righteous? _____

    _____

  - How was God merciful to you? _____

    _____

  - What perspective did you gain as a result? _____

    _____

  - How have you been appointed by God to serve going forward? _____

    _____

- Read 1 Corinthians 13:1-3. How does love help you guard against self-righteous thinking/behavior? _____

  _____

  _____

- Read Romans 2:12-13. Realistically, what active role does the Word of God play in your daily life? _____

  _____

  _____

- What are risks associated with not reading/studying/praying God's Word each day?

  - _____   • _____   • _____

- 2 Peter 2:21 was written to warn of the dangers of false teachers, yet provides powerful truth for all men. Considering your own heart, answer the following questions in light of this wisdom.

  - What absolute truth of Scripture do you know in your head but not in your heart? _____

    _____

  - What are dangers of not applying 2 Peter 2:21? _____

    _____

  - What impact has neglecting 2 Peter 2:21 had on your family? _____

    _____

- Read Matthew 9:10-13. Jesus wants us to "go and learn" what regarding self-righteousness? _____

_____

_____

- How are you instructed to view the righteousness of others compared to yourself? _____

_____

_____

- What sets you apart from those who have not believed the truth of God's Word? _____

_____

_____

- How can you teach this invaluable lesson to your children? _____

_____

_____

_____

> "The knowledge of God is also the great hope of sinners. O child of earth, if you knew Him better, you would fly to Him! If you understood how gracious He is, you would seek Him! If you could have any idea of His holiness, you would loathe your self-righteousness! If you knew anything of His power, you would not venture to contend with Him. If you knew anything of His Grace, you would not hesitate to yield yourself to Him. The more God reveals Himself to you and the more you know of God, the more are you in the way of hope and mercy!"
>
> - Charles Spurgeon -

- What is your greatest takeaway from today's study? _____

_____

_____

_____

> "For by the grace given to me I say to everyone among you not to think of himself more highly than he ought, but to think with sober judgment, each according to the measure of faith God has assigned."
>
> - Romans 12:3 -

- What does this verse mean to you? _____

_____

_____

_____

# Pride - Day 1

Pride is arguably the biggest issue men fall victim to and the first men reject as a much-needed area of improvement in their lives, which is the very nature of pride itself! Pride declares such foolishness as "I don't have a problem;" "I'm right, you're wrong;" and "I don't need any help." Pride feasts upon a desire for supreme control and can easily cause a man to rely on himself rather than God. It is a silent killer like cancer, permeating throughout the heart and mind to spread discreetly and destroy from within. The only remedy is a heavy dose of modesty which comes through complete surrender to God and the disciplined regimen of seeking opportunities to humble ourselves. Imagine how many lives would be transformed if we applied these truths to our hearts and rejected sinful pride before it took root!

- What is sinful pride? _____
  _____

- What does sinful pride look like in your own life? How does it manifest itself? Be specific.
  - _____
  - _____
  - _____

- What words best describe a man who is prideful?
  - _____   •  _____   •  _____   •  _____
  - Give an example where you have learned Proverbs 16:18. _____
    _____
    _____

- Read Isaiah 13:11. What difference does it make knowing how passionately God opposes selfish pride and arrogance? _____
  _____

- How does pride typically drive deep wedges between you and your wife during conflict resolution? _____
  _____
  _____
  _____

- Read Ecclesiastes 7:8. What does it mean to be patient in Spirit vs. proud in Spirit? _____
  _____
  _____

- Read 2 Chronicles 7:14. What does humbling yourself look like toward your wife and children?

  - Wife: _____

  - Wife: _____

  - Children: _____

  - Children: _____

  - What impact does this have on your spiritual walk? _____
    _____
    _____

- How has pride caused you to reject that you have a problem with sin in your life? _____
  _____
  _____

> "The fact is, the higher up we find ourselves in terms of power, influence, and wealth – the more people look up to us – the more vulnerable we are to pride and self-deceit, and the more prone we are to be blind to our spiritual needs and deficiencies. Once we are established in a position of influence, we have a reputation to maintain. We have a lot to lose if we get honest about our real spiritual needs. For most of us, the subtle encroachment of pride is more dangerous, and more likely to render us useless to God and others, than any other kind of failure."
>
> - Nancy Leigh DeMoss -

- What is your greatest takeaway from today's study? _____
  _____
  _____
  _____

> "Clothe yourselves, all of you, with humility toward one another,
> for 'God opposes the proud but gives grace to the humble."
>
> - 1 Peter 5:5 -

- What does this verse mean to you? _____
  _____
  _____
  _____

# Pride - Day 2

- What are you most proud of (positively) concerning your wife and children?

|            WIFE            |          CHILDREN          |
| -------------------------- | -------------------------- |
| • _____ | • _____ |
| • _____ | • _____ |
| • _____ | • _____ |
| • _____ | • _____ |

- • Have you taken time to express these things? _____ Why or why not? _____

    _____

    _____

- What are benefits of leading your family in humility rather than intimidation or expectation?

    - • _____        • _____

    - • _____        • _____

- How have you witnessed your prideful tendencies (righteous vs. sinful) rubbing off on your children?

    - • Righteous: _____

    - • Righteous: _____

    - • Sinful: _____

    - • Sinful: _____

- Read Philippians 2:3. What emotions stir in your heart when you read this verse?

    - • _____   • _____   • _____

    - • Who do you need to seek forgiveness from most concerning your selfishness? _____

- Have you ever given your wife permission to hold you accountable? _____ Why or why not? _____

    _____

    _____

- • What specifically do you need to be held accountable about now? _____

    _____

    _____

- Read Psalm 51. What four points of wisdom can you apply to your life from the brokenness of King David's prayer to gain victory over pride and arrogance?

  - _____

  - _____

  - _____

  - _____

  - Which verse convicts your heart most? _____ Why? _____
  _____
  _____

  - Which verse is most encouraging to you? _____ Why? _____
  _____
  _____

> "If our theology does not quicken the conscience and soften the heart, it actually hardens both; if it does not encourage the commitment of faith, it reinforces the detachment of unbelief; if it fails to promote humility, it inevitably feeds pride."
>
> - J.I. Packer -
>
> "Pride is the sin we cannot see in ourselves and yet so detest in others."
>
> - Kent Hughes -

- What is your greatest takeaway from today's study? _____
_____
_____
_____

> "Love the Lord, all you his saints!
> The Lord preserves the faithful but abundantly repays the one who acts in pride."
> - Psalm 31:23 -

- What does this verse mean to you? _____
_____
_____
_____

# Personal Accountability - Day 1

Accountability is one of the least understood concepts in the Bible. Most Christians agree they need it but few implement it, mainly because it's messy and convicting. A man must let his guard down, be vulnerable, and take his lumps. However, pointing out the faults of others is much easier than facing our own shortcomings. Personally, lack of true Biblical accountability plunged me deep into hypocrisy. Although I had accountable relationships, I conditionally manipulated them through a facade of calculated (safe) transparency rather than unabandoned (risky) vulnerability. Self-protection will cause a man to do just about anything to protect his fragile ego and pride. Therefore, we must overcome fear and remember we are no longer slaves to our flesh but purchased by God through Jesus Christ.

- Personal accountability begins with surrender and acknowledging you need help living according to God's Word. What holds you back from asking for help? _____

_____

_____

- Anything in your life can drive a wedge in your heart if it takes higher priority than your faith, marriage or family. What specific areas do you need to guard against which consume your heart?

  - _____

  - _____

  - _____

- Read Proverbs 27:17. What areas of life are you open to accountability vs. closed off?

| OPEN TO ACCOUNTABILITY | CLOSED OFF FROM ACCOUNTABILITY |
|---|---|
| • _____ | • _____ |
| • _____ | • _____ |
| • _____ | • _____ |

- Read Romans 14:10-12. What are you fearful/scared of being held accountable for on judgment day? _____

_____

- What drives your posture of fear? _____

_____

- How can your wife begin to pray for you in this area? _____

_____

- No one understands how another woman thinks, feels and acts better than your wife. What warnings has she brought to your attention concerning relationships you have with other women?

  - Warning: _____

  - Warning: _____

  - Warning: _____

  - How have you reacted/responded? _____
  _____

  - What tempts you to disregard her accountability? _____
  _____

  - How do you discern whether her accountability is constructive/helpful vs. attacking/mothering? ___
  _____
  _____
  _____

> *"A man who confesses his sins in the presence of a brother knows that he is no longer alone with himself; he experiences the presence of God in the reality of the other person. As long as I am by myself in the confession of my sins, everything remains in the clear, but in the presence of a brother, the sin has to be brought into the light."*
>
> *- Dietrich Bonhoeffer -*

- What is your greatest takeaway from today's study? _____
_____
_____
_____

> *"Now we know that whatever the law says it speaks to those who are under the law, so that every mouth may be stopped, and the whole world may be held accountable to God."*
>
> *- Romans 3:19 -*

- What does this verse mean to you? _____
_____
_____
_____

# Personal Accountability – Day 2

- Read James 2:10. What wisdom can you glean from this truth? _____
_____

- Read Matthew 12:36 and answer how you can guard/tame your tongue.

  - Do you feel it is okay to use profanities? _____ Why or why not? _____
  _____

  - What words do you use when you're frustrated? _____

  - What words do you use when you're angry? _____

  - What words do you use when your sexual desires are not being met? _____

  - What words do you use when you're disciplining your children? _____
  _____

  - What impact does writing these answers down on paper have on your heart? _____
  _____

  - What do you need to repent of concerning the words you speak? _____
  _____

- Most men struggle to maintain sexual purity in their lives. What boundaries can you put into place to guard your heart and mind from twisting God's design for sex in the life/marriage of a believer?

  - Internet Browsing: _____

  - Social Media: _____

  - TV/Movies: _____

  - Culture (In general): _____

  - Self-Gratification: _____

- No accountability partner can replace your wife because she should know you better than anyone else. What fears, doubts or reservations hinder you from sharing your private self with her?

  - _____     - _____

  - _____     - _____

  - How can she come alongside you to help? _____
  _____

- Every man needs accountability partners, yet very few pursue one in their lives. Who provides you personal accountability and what level of transparency do you share? NOTE: If you do not currently have an active accountability partner, who can you ask and for what emphasis?

  - EXAMPLE:  Who: <u>DAVID</u>  Emphasis of Accountability? <u>Sexual Purity (Am I bouncing my eyes when I see attractive women in public? Am I viewing any form of pornography? Am I self-gratifying? Am I using sexual innuendos? Am I placing unrealistic expectations on sexual  intimacy with my wife? Am I closing off any semblance of flirtation with other women in the workplace?)</u>

  - Who? _____ Emphasis of Accountability? _____
    _____
    _____

  - Who? _____ Emphasis of Accountability? _____
    _____
    _____

  - What is your biggest fear about having an accountability partner? _____
    _____
    _____

> "The conscience...is not infallible. Nor is it a source of revelation about right and wrong.
> Its role is not to teach you moral and ethical ideals, but to hold you accountable
> to the highest standards of right and wrong you know."
>
> - John MacArthur -

- What is your greatest takeaway from today's study? _____
  _____
  _____
  _____

> "Two are better than one, because they have a good reward for their toil. For if they fall, one will
> lift up his fellow. But woe to him who is alone when he falls and has not another to lift him up!"
>
> - Ecclesiastes 4:9-10 -

- What does this verse mean to you? _____
  _____
  _____
  _____

# Self-Control - Day 1

Within character attributes, self-control is arguably the pearl of great price. Without it, man is held captive to his sin and enslaved by tempestuous attacks which inevitably overcome his will. No man is strong enough in his own power to resist the schemes of the devil, but only by the power of the Holy Spirit can he turn away from sin and embrace self-control. Not a day goes by where I don't struggle with exhibiting self-control, but I also know the power of its absence and the destructive wake it can leave behind. Lack of self-control will bring a man to his lowest point without fail. However, self-control can surely save his life if he is willing to surrender his pride and humble himself unto Christ. The power of the cross is man's only source of strength when it comes to gaining self-control over sin, not his own will.

- How would you define self-control? _____
  _____

- How can a man have self-control yet surrender complete control of his life to God? _____
  _____
  _____

- In what public and private areas of your behavior do you struggle exhibiting self-control most?

|  PUBLIC  |  PRIVATE  |
|---|---|
| • _____ | • _____ |
| • _____ | • _____ |
| • _____ | • _____ |

- Read Proverbs 25:28. Give an example where lack of self-control has taught you an invaluable life lesson. What did you learn? _____
  _____
  _____

  - What regrets do you have regarding your behavior? _____
    _____
    _____

- Read 2 Timothy 1:7. What fears do you struggle with in your marriage which manifest themselves in lack of self-control?

  • _____     • _____

  • _____     • _____

- Read Titus 2:1-10. What character attributes does the apostle Paul associate self-control with?

- _____  • _____  • _____  • _____

- _____  • _____  • _____  • _____

- _____  • _____  • _____  • _____

- What is God communicating to you from this list? _____
  _____
  _____

- Which qualities listed above demonstrate your strengths? _____
  _____
  _____

- Which qualities listed above demonstrate your weaknesses? _____
  _____
  _____

> "Our minds are mental greenhouses where unlawful thoughts, once planted,
> are nurtured and watered before being transplanted into the real world of unlawful
> actions... These actions are savored in the mind long before they are enjoyed in reality.
> The thought life, then, is our first line of defense in the battle of self-control."
>
> - Jerry Bridges -

- What is your greatest takeaway from today's study? _____
  _____
  _____
  _____

> "I know that nothing good lives in me, that is, in my sinful nature.
> For I have the desire to do what is good, but I cannot carry it out. For what I do is not
> the good I want to do; no, the evil I do not want to do – this I keep on doing!"
>
> - Romans 7:18-19 -

- What does this verse mean to you? _____
  _____
  _____
  _____

# Self-Control ~ Day 2

- Read 1 Corinthians 9:24-27 and give an example how you can improve self-control in the following areas of your life/marriage.

  - Conflict: _____
    _____

  - Finances: _____
    _____

  - Intimacy: _____
    _____

  - Communication: _____
    _____

  - Prioritization: _____
    _____

  - Expectations: _____
    _____

  - Personal Accountability: _____
    _____

- What are potential dangers of using 1 Corinthians 7:5 for selfish gain within your marriage?

  - _____     • _____

  - _____     • _____

  - How can this verse strengthen your spiritual intimacy? _____
    _____

  - In what ways are YOU depriving your wife sexually? _____
    _____

- What fruit is harvested when you honor your wife by exhibiting self-control within your sinful bents?

  - _____     • _____     • _____

  - What risk are you taking when you use the excuse, "I can't change. It's just the way I am?" _____
    _____
    _____

- Read Judges 14-16. What was the root issue in Samson failing to use self-control?

    - His marriage: _____

    - The riddle: _____

    - 300 foxes: _____

    - Donkey's jawbone: _____

    - His thirst: _____

    - His lust: _____

    - His lies to Delilah: _____

    - His confession: _____

    - His revenge: _____

    - What is Samson's legacy though? _____
      _____

"People do not drift toward holiness. Apart from grace-driven effort, people do not gravitate toward godliness, prayer, obedience to Scripture, faith, and delight in the Lord. We drift toward compromise and call it tolerance; we drift toward disobedience and call it freedom; we drift toward superstition and call it faith. We cherish the indiscipline of lost self-control and call it relaxation; we slouch toward prayerlessness and delude ourselves into thinking we have escaped legalism; we slide toward godlessness and convince ourselves we have been liberated."

- D.A. Carson -

- What is your greatest takeaway from today's study? _____
  _____
  _____
  _____

"Every athlete exercises self-control in all things. They do it to receive a perishable wreath, but we an imperishable. So I do not run aimlessly; I do not box as one beating the air. But I discipline my body and keep it under control, lest after preaching to others I myself should be disqualified."

- 1 Corinthians 9:25-27 -

- What does this verse mean to you? _____
  _____
  _____
  _____

# Checkpoint 4

It is important to not get too far ahead of ourselves when navigating the wilderness and lose sight of how far we've come. Therefore, checkpoints have been created as opportunities to stop and reflect upon where we began this journey of faith and self-examination, what we've learned thus far by studying these specific topics, how God has transformed our hearts to this point, and what impact this study is having on our wives and children. In essence, these checkpoints are opportunities to establish spiritual markers which will act as trail markers on our wilderness journey, reminding us of God's provision and faithfulness to "restore the years the swarming locust has eaten" (Joel 2:25). Keep in mind, mountain-top perspective is most appreciated when we consider the valley from which we came and celebrate our progress made.

- Over the past 4-weeks, which Scripture passages you've studied have gripped your heart the most?

  - _____    - _____

  - _____    - _____

- Over the past 4-weeks, what has CONVICTED you most from each of the topics you've studied?

  - Self-Righteousness: _____
  _____

  - Pride: _____
  _____

  - Personal Accountability: _____
  _____

  - Self-Control: _____
  _____

- Over the past 4-weeks, what has ENCOURAGED you most from each of the topics you've studied?

  - Self-Righteousness: _____
  _____

  - Pride: _____
  _____

  - Personal Accountability: _____
  _____

  - Self-Control: _____
  _____

- How have you been INSPIRED to be a better husband to your wife over the past 4-weeks? _____

_____

_____

_____

- How have you been INSPIRED to be a better father to your children over the past 4-weeks? _____

_____

_____

_____

- How have you been INSPIRED to be a better man (in general) over the past 4-weeks? _____

_____

_____

_____

> "Man never achieves a clear knowledge of himself unless he has first looked upon God's face,
> and then descends from contemplating Him to scrutinize himself.
> For we always seem to ourselves righteous and upright and wise and holy –
> this pride is innate in all of us – unless by clear proofs we stand convinced
> of our own unrighteousness, foulness, folly, and impurity.
> Moreover, we are not thus convinced if we look merely to ourselves and not also to the Lord,
> who is the sole standard by which this judgment must be measured ."
>
> - John Calvin -

- Create one practical goal per topic you plan to achieve moving forward and your inspiration for choosing it.
    - Self-Righteousness: _____
        - Inspiration: _____
    - Pride: _____
        - Inspiration: _____
    - Personal Accountability: _____
        - Inspiration: _____
    - Self-Control: _____
        - Inspiration: _____

# Culture ~ Day 1

Culture seeks our heart's devotion at all cost. Whether it be internet, social media outlets, smartphones, television, movies, radio, billboards, magazines, etc., opportunities for messages which compromise our values and destroy our psyche are infinite. The question is to what extent are we willing to place safeguards in our lives? Insulating ourselves from culture is not the answer because we're to live in the world, not conform to it. Easier said than done, though, for Satan wants nothing more than to pull us back into our sinful tendencies. Therefore, we must guard our hearts, protect our minds, and feed upon the absolute truth of God's Holy Word daily. Culture only promises false satisfaction, but the man who boldly confronts it head-on rather than passively ignoring it will ultimately survive its deadly snare.

- What cultural messages do you actively fight to protect your family from?

    - _____  • _____  • _____

- In what ways do you find your family susceptible to materialism, covetousness and comparison?

    - Materialism: _____
      _____

    - Covetousness: _____
      _____

    - Comparison: _____
      _____

- What methods or outlets do you personally use to escape from the pressures of life?

    - _____  • _____

    - _____  • _____

- Read Matthew 18:7. Why is it necessary temptations arise in your life? _____
  _____
  _____

    - What temptation weighs heaviest against your marriage? _____
      Why? _____
      _____

    - What measures have you taken to safeguard yourself from this temptation? _____
      _____
      _____

- Read Mark 4:14-19. Practically-speaking, how is God's Word being choked out of your daily life? _____
  _____
  _____
  _____

- What cultural ideas are creating expectations within your marriage?

  - What? _____ How? _____
    _____

  - What? _____ How? _____
    _____

  - Why are expectations cancerous to a wife? _____
    _____
    _____

> "We live in a world where truth is relative. According to most, there is no absolute standard to determine right from wrong because truth is ever-changing and subjectively suited to personal opinions and popular culture. Most want to believe this because at our core we want to be autonomous without any accountability and restraints. We want to be God. We want to be the sole arbitrator to determine right from wrong. So to bolster support for this driving tendency, many have used the Word of God for their justification. They have erroneously taken Jesus' words in Matthew 7 not to judge as their shield for critique-free sinful behavior."
>
> - Randy Smith -

- What is your greatest takeaway from today's study? _____
  _____
  _____
  _____

> "Do not be conformed to this world, but be transformed by the renewal of your mind, that by testing you may discern what is the will of God, what is good and acceptable and perfect."
>
> - Romans 12:2 -

- What does this verse mean to you? _____
  _____
  _____
  _____

# Culture - Day 2

- Read 1 Corinthians 1:27-29. What foolish thing of this world has God used to shame you most?

  - What: _____

    _____

  - How: _____

    _____

- Read Galatians 4:8-9. Why is it difficult to break away from sins which formerly enslaved you? _____

  _____

  _____

- What hobbies, interests or activities distract you from spending quality time with your family?

  - _____  •  _____  •  _____

  - What regrets do you have concerning the time you've invested in your marriage? _____

    _____

    _____

  - What regrets do you have concerning the time you've invested in your parenting? _____

    _____

    _____

- What sinful aspect of today's culture are you most fearful your children will fall victim to?

  - What: _____

  - Why: _____

    _____

  - How has this sinful bent affected you personally? _____

    _____

- Read 1 Corinthians 1:18-25. Why is preaching Christ-crucified viewed as both a stumbling block and folly to our present culture? _____

  _____

  - How are you presently preaching Christ-crucified? _____

    _____

- Read Philippians 2:12-18. How are you called to be light within a perverse culture bent against God? _____
  _____
  _____

- How can you encourage your wife to do the same? _____
  _____

  - How can you encourage your children to do the same? _____
    _____

- Considering where you live, what two things about the surrounding culture do you love most?

  - _____    • _____

  - How can you channel that same passion into evangelism? _____
    _____
    _____

> "Philosophical pluralism is the ideology that refuses to allow any single religion or worldview to claim an exclusive hold on the truth. It denies that there are any absolutes. It insists that all religions and worldviews must be seen as equally valid...To suggest otherwise is to be arrogant and intolerant. No religion can claim to be superior to any other. You may practice your faith as long as you realize it is only one of many true faiths. If what you believe is true at all, it is only relatively true... [But] at the same time that philosophical pluralism denies other religions the right to lay claim to the truth, it presents its own worldview as the absolute truth."
>
> - Philip Graham Ryken -

- What is your greatest takeaway from today's study? _____
  _____
  _____

> "Let no one deceive himself. If anyone among you thinks that he is wise in this age,
> let him become a fool that he may become wise. For the wisdom of this world is folly with God."
>
> - 1 Corinthians 3:18-19 -

- What does this verse mean to you? _____
  _____
  _____
  _____

# Fatherly Influence - Day 1

Good or bad, family plays a major role in our lives. What we witnessed and experienced as children shaped our construct of behavior to the extent we can trace tendencies back to our family upbringing. The danger is not to use family as a crutch excuse for justifying sinful behavior. Family influence also plays a huge role in cutting parental ties when we reach adulthood, as well as the impact of sibling dynamics, order of birth, blended families, etc. Family is incredibly complex and messy and can test the character of any man and his marriage. Therefore, we must learn to implement healthy boundaries regarding family and more importantly, recognize and understand how our fathers especially have influenced our behavior for better or worse. As men, who we are today is directly and indirectly impacted by fatherly influence.

- What character attributes describe your father (CIRCLE: biological, adopted or step) growing up?

    - _____  • _____  • _____  • _____

    - What was his greatest strength? _____

    _____

    - What was his greatest weakness? _____

    _____

- What is your lasting impression of how your father interacted with family members growing up?

    - Toward Your Mother: _____

    _____

    - Toward Your Siblings: _____

    _____

    - Toward You: _____

    _____

- How would you describe your relationship with your father currently? (Note: If you did not have any fatherly influence, describe the impact that made on you.) _____

    _____

    _____

- Read Exodus 34:6-7. Do you tend to see yourself breaking away from the mold your father gave you, or are you falling into the same sinful patterns he struggled with? _____ How so? _____

    _____

    _____

- Read Proverbs 13:24. What are blessings and curses of this verse from your personal experience?

  - As a son (blessing): _____

  - As a son (curse): _____

  - As a father (blessing): _____

  - As a father (curse): _____

- Read Psalm 103:13. What benefits come from being a compassionate father toward your children?

  - _____        - _____

  - _____        - _____

  - Why is compassion such an important trait of a good father? _____
    _____

  - In what ways do you struggle being a compassionate father? _____
    _____

"A famous cigarette billboard pictures a curly-headed, bronze-faced, muscular macho with a cigarette hanging out the side of his mouth. The sign says, "Where a man belongs." That is a lie. Where a man belongs is at the bedside of his children, leading in devotion and prayer. Where a man belongs is leading his family to the house of God. Where a man belongs is up early and alone with God seeking vision and direction for the family...The happiest and holiest children in the world are the children whose fathers succeed in winning both their tender affection and their reverential and loving fear. And they are the children who will come to understand most easily the mystery of the fatherhood of God."

- John Piper -

- What is your greatest takeaway from today's study? _____
  _____
  _____
  _____

"Train up a child in the way he should go; even when he is old he will not depart from it."
- Proverbs 22:6 -

- What does this verse mean to you? _____
  _____
  _____
  _____

# Fatherly Influence - Day 2

- Read Ephesians 3:14-19. What difference does it make knowing God has specifically appointed you to your earthly family? _____

  _____

  - What role do you play and for what purpose? _____

    _____

- What example (+/-) did your father provide regarding the roles of a Godly husband/father?

  - Prayer: _____

  - Bible Study: _____

  - Provision: _____

  - Integrity: _____

  - Character: _____

  - Respect: _____

- Read Colossians 3:21 and Ephesians 6:4. What dangers result from provoking your children?

  - _____   - _____

  - _____   - _____

- Read Hebrews 12:7-11. What encouragement can you glean from this Scripture passage? _____

  _____

  _____

- Read 3 John 1:4. What emotions (+/-) stir in your heart regarding this verse?

  - _____   - _____   - _____

  - What makes this so personal to you? _____

    _____

- Based on your father's example, how do you seek reconciliation when you offend your family?

  - Wife: _____

    _____

  - Children: _____

    _____

- In what way do you feel your father was most present vs. most absent in your life? How so?

  - Present: _____

    _____

  - Absent: _____

    _____

- What challenges do you struggle with as you strive to lead your family spiritually?

  - _____

  - _____

  - _____

> "If you fail, father, to teach your son to fear God, the devil will teach him to hate God.
> If you fail to teach your son to guard his mind, the devil will gladly teach him to have an open mind.
> If you fail to teach your son to obey his parents, the devil will teach him to rebel and break his parent's
> heart. If you fail to teach your son to select his companions, the devil will gladly choose them for him.
> If you fail to teach your son to control his body, the devil will teach him to give it over completely
> to lust. If you fail to teach your son to enjoy the marriage partner that God has given him,
> the devil will teach him to destroy the marriage. If you fail to teach your son to watch his words,
> the devil will fill his mouth with filth. If you fail to teach your son to pursue his work,
> the devil will make his laziness a tool of hell. If you fail to teach your son to manage his money,
> the devil will teach him to waste it on riotous living. And if you fail to teach your son
> to love his neighbor, the devil will gladly teach him to love only himself."
>
> - John MacArthur -

- What is your greatest takeaway from today's study? _____

  _____

  _____

  _____

> "My son, do not despise the Lord's discipline or be weary of his reproof,
> for the Lord reproves him whom he loves, as a father the son in whom he delights."
>
> - Proverbs 3:11-12 -

- What does this verse mean to you? _____

  _____

  _____

  _____

# Change ~ Day 1

The honeymoon is over the day we realize we cannot change our wives. While it is human nature to hope or wish for positive changes to occur, there is no guarantee our wives will behave how we wish they would or vice versa. Change is a personal decision only God can bring to fruition and the key to change begins and ends with us, not our wives! Moreover, we're not called to be their personal Holy Spirit. Rather, we must learn to not "quench the Spirit" while their hearts are transformed by God. It is also just as dangerous to use manipulation to force change to occur, which is not leadership but selfishness God will ultimately judge. Therefore, we must ask ourselves, "Do I want my wife to change so I don't have to, or is there heart change I need to address and reconcile in myself first and foremost?"

- If you could change anything about yourself, what would it be?

  - _____     - _____

  - _____     - _____

  - What pattern do you see in your responses? _____
    _____

- If you could change anything about your wife, what would it be?

  - _____     - _____

  - _____     - _____

  - What pattern do you see in your responses? _____
    _____

- Read Matthew 21:28-32. How are you guilty of refusing to change in your life? _____
  _____
  _____

  - Why do actions speak louder than words? _____
    _____

- What are the risks of hard-heartedness toward change?

  - _____    - _____    - _____

- Read Numbers 23:19 and Malachi 3:6. How is God's unwavering nature reassuring as you examine your attitude toward personal change? _____
  _____

- What fear, worry and doubt do you struggle with most as you examine your attitude toward change?

  - Fear: _____

  - Worry: _____

  - Doubt: _____

- What role does shame and regret over former sins play in your ability to change now? _____
  _____
  _____

- Give an example how God has used your wife to encourage positive change in you. _____
  _____
  _____
  _____
  _____

> "I never have any difficulty believing in miracles,
> since I experienced the miracle of a change in my own heart."
>
> - Augustine -
>
> "Consider what you owe to His immutability.
> Though you have changed a thousand times, He has not changed once."
>
> - Charles Spurgeon -

- What is your greatest takeaway from today's study? _____
  _____
  _____
  _____

> "Who is like the wise? And who knows the interpretation of a thing?
> A man's wisdom makes his face shine, and the hardness of his face is changed."
>
> - Ecclesiastes 8:1 -

- What does this verse mean to you? _____
  _____
  _____
  _____

# Change ~ Day 2

- Read Daniel 2:20-22. What role does God play in the process of change? _____
  _____

- In order for change to come full circle, it must be accepted as authentic by others. Give an example where you believe you have changed, but others continue to question your genuineness. _____
  _____
  _____

- What are potential risks of owning your sin but continuing to wear it like a scarlet letter?
  - _____        - _____
  - _____        - _____

- How can Isaiah 43:25 help you move on from habitual sin in your life? _____
  _____
  _____

- Read Matthew 7:1-2. Practically-speaking, how are you casting judgment on your wife?
  - _____
  - _____

- How is your unwillingness to accept genuine, Biblical changes that your wife is making creating a wedge in your marriage? _____
  _____
  _____

  - Is there justifiable reason to hold any sin over your wife? _____ Why or why not? _____
    _____
    _____

- Read Matthew 7:15-20. Which bad fruit clearly demonstrates what manipulation looks like?
  - _____        - _____        - _____
  - _____        - _____        - _____

  - What is the goal of manipulation? _____
    _____

- What tactics do you commonly use to manipulate change in your wife and children?

<u>WIFE</u>                                                    <u>CHILDREN</u>

- _____                    - _____
- _____                    - _____
- _____                    - _____

- How can Matthew 7:3-5 hold you accountable from judging others? _____
_____
_____

- Read Ecclesiastes 3:1-8. What season of change do you currently find yourself in?

  - Personally: _____
  _____

  - Professionally: _____
  _____

> "The exercise of the mouth cannot change the heart. Your sin is like a prostitute. You are speaking against your lover in public but embracing her in the bedroom. She is not particular about being run down in public if she can have your full attention in private... Confession by itself is not repentance. Confession moves the lips; repentance moves the heart. Naming an act as evil before God is not the same as leaving it. Though your confession may be honest and emotional, it is not enough unless it expresses a true change of heart... If a man turns from sin without turning to God, he will find his sin has only changed its name and is hidden behind his pride."
>
> - Jim Elliff -

- What is your greatest takeaway from today's study? _____
_____
_____
_____

> "Jesus Christ is the same yesterday and today and forever."
> - Hebrews 13:8 -

- What does this verse mean to you? _____
_____
_____
_____

# Forgiveness - Day 1

Forgiveness is an essential trait of a Godly man, husband and father, for we have assurance of salvation because God ultimately forgave us and we are called to forgive others as well. Why then is it so difficult to forgive at times? Why do we succumb to forgetfulness, failing to remember that grace and mercy are pillars of forgiveness? If we desire to be Godly men, we must begin each day thanking God for His forgiveness, then paying it forward by forgiving others. If we're honest, there are countless times our families have forgiven us when we've least deserved it or were too stubborn to recognize our sins and own our mistakes. Therefore, let us never forget how blessed we are to have patient wives and children who endure our shortcomings/failures and love us despite them... and may we freely forgive in return.

- What does it mean to forgive someone in the following aspects?

  - Emotionally: _____

  - Physically: _____

  - Relationally: _____

  - Spiritually: _____

- Read Psalm 51. What nuggets of wisdom can you glean from David's prayer of forgiveness?

  - _____

  - _____

  - _____

  - What personal experience do you have which relates to David's spirit of repentance? _____
    _____
    _____

- Which elements of your sinful past do you struggle forgiving yourself?

  - _____ • _____ • _____

  - Have you repented of your sins and asked God to wash away all your iniquity? _____ Why or why not? _____
    _____

- If God has forgiven your sins, what holds you back from letting go of the past? _____
  _____
  _____

- How does Satan use guilt and shame to enslave you to former sins God has already forgiven? _____
  _____
  _____

- Why is Isaiah 43:25 one of the most encouraging promises in Scripture? _____
  _____
  _____

- What emotions stir in you when you reflect upon the forgiveness God has shown throughout your life?
  - _____  · _____  · _____  · _____
  - _____  · _____  · _____  · _____

    - Why is it important to remember spiritual markers of forgiveness in particular? _____
      _____
      _____

> "Forgiveness is not that stripe which says, "I will forgive, but not forget."
> It is not to bury the hatchet with the handle sticking out of the ground,
> so you can grasp it the minute you want it."
>
> - D.L. Moody -
>
> "Every man should keep a fair-sized cemetery in which to bury the faults of his friends."
>
> - Henry Ward Beecher -

- What is your greatest takeaway from today's study? _____
  _____
  _____
  _____

> "If my people who are called by my name humble themselves, and pray and seek my face and turn
> from their wicked ways, then I will hear from heaven and will forgive their sin and heal their land."
> - 2 Chronicles 7:14 -

- What does this verse mean to you? _____
  _____
  _____
  _____

# Forgiveness – Day 2

- Read Matthew 6:14-15. What are potential dangers of withholding forgiveness from your wife?

  - Toward Her: _____

  - Toward God: _____

  - Toward Yourself: _____

  - Toward Your Children: _____

- Marriage bubbles to the surface numerous issues (whether substantiated or not) we hold against our wives rather than forgive. What specifically are you holding onto and struggling to forgive?

  - _____     - _____

  - _____     - _____

- Why is it critical to seek forgiveness directly from your children when you've sinned against them? _____
  _____
  _____

  - What is the impact of NOT practicing this discipline? _____
  _____

- How can your wife help you become a man who embraces forgiveness rather than avoids it? _____
  _____
  _____

- Read James 2:14-17. What benefits come from modeling forgiveness rather than preaching it?

  - _____     - _____

  - _____     - _____

- Read 2 Corinthians 7:10. What distinguishes Godly grief from worldly grief? _____
  _____

- Do you believe all sins are forgivable by God? _____ Why or why not? _____
  _____

  - If not, which sins are unforgiveable? _____
  _____

- Read Matthew 18:21-35 where Jesus compares God's forgiveness vs. man's.

  - How do you relate to the king? _____

  _____

  - How do you relate to the servant? _____

  _____

  - How can you apply this to your marriage? _____

  _____

- Read Matthew 18:21-22. What residual impact can this passage have on others if you apply it? _____

_____

_____

_____

> "Scripture never tells us to forgive ourselves. When we try to "forgive" ourselves, we are attempting the impossible. Forgiveness assumes an innocent party has been wronged, and it is the job of the person who has been wronged to forgive. The offending party is the one that receives forgiveness. We are the offender; God is the one who has been wronged, since our sin is rebellion against Him. By focusing on forgiving ourselves, we have taken the spotlight off of God and pointed it at us – making it doubly difficult to let go of our sin! He has forgiven us. We must simply receive that forgiveness and rest in it. That means releasing those sins we want to hold on to, refusing to revisit them in our minds, and allowing the truth of our forgiveness to cover us with His peace. Absolution from the Lord is far more powerful than absolution from oneself."
>
> - Charles Swindoll -

- What is your greatest takeaway from today's study? _____

_____

_____

_____

> "Judge not, and you will not be judged; condemn not, and you will not be condemned; forgive, and you will be forgiven."
>
> - Luke 6:37 -

- What does this verse mean to you? _____

_____

_____

_____

# Checkpoint 5

It is important to not get too far ahead of ourselves when navigating the wilderness and lose sight of how far we've come. Therefore, checkpoints have been created as opportunities to stop and reflect upon where we began this journey of faith and self-examination, what we've learned thus far by studying these specific topics, how God has transformed our hearts to this point, and what impact this study is having on our wives and children. In essence, these checkpoints are opportunities to establish spiritual markers which will act as trail markers on our wilderness journey, reminding us of God's provision and faithfulness to "restore the years the swarming locust has eaten" (Joel 2:25). Keep in mind, mountain-top perspective is most appreciated when we consider the valley from which we came and celebrate our progress made.

- Over the past 4-weeks, which Scripture passages you've studied have gripped your heart the most?

  - _____        - _____

  - _____        - _____

- Over the past 4-weeks, what has CONVICTED you most from each of the topics you've studied?

  - Culture: _____
  _____

  - Fatherly Influence: _____
  _____

  - Change: _____
  _____

  - Forgiveness: _____
  _____

- Over the past 4-weeks, what has ENCOURAGED you most from each of the topics you've studied?

  - Culture: _____
  _____

  - Fatherly Influence: _____
  _____

  - Change: _____
  _____

  - Forgiveness: _____
  _____

- How have you been INSPIRED to be a better husband to your wife over the past 4-weeks? _____

_____

_____

_____

- How have you been INSPIRED to be a better father to your children over the past 4-weeks? _____

_____

_____

_____

- How have you been INSPIRED to be a better man (in general) over the past 4-weeks? _____

_____

_____

_____

> *"Genuine sanctification is a thing that can be seen."*
>
> - J.C. Ryle -
>
> *"Our Lord does not promise to change life for us; He does not promise to remove difficulties and trials and problems and tribulations; He does not say that He is going to cut out all the thorns and leave the roses with their wonderful perfume. No; He faces life realistically, and tells us that these are things to which the flesh is heir, and which are bound to come. But He assures us that we can so know Him that, whatever happens, we need never be frightened, we need never be alarmed."*
>
> - D. Martyn Lloyd-Jones -

- Create one practical goal per topic you plan to achieve moving forward and your inspiration for choosing it.

  - Culture: _____

    - Inspiration: _____

  - Fatherly Influence: _____

    - Inspiration: _____

  - Change: _____

    - Inspiration: _____

  - Forgiveness: _____

    - Inspiration: _____

# Congratulations!
## You've made it half-way!

Continue the journey with Wilderness Survival, Volume 2...

How Men Survive Isolation & Defeat The Enemy

# Wilderness Survival
## ~ Volume 2 ~

## Daniel Ploof

JourneyIntoTheWilderness.com

Made in the USA
Monee, IL
19 December 2022

22968311R00057